The Butterflies of Colchester and North East Essex

By
Ted Benton and Joe Firmin
with additional material by Ian Rose

Photographs by Ted Benton and Ian Rose

A history, natural history and guide

Published by Colchester Natural History Society, 2002
Printed and bound by Palladian Press, Colchester

CONTENTS

© Colchester Natural History Society
© Photography Ted Benton and Ian Rose
Front cover designed and photographed by David Warner

ISBN 0-9516312-1-7

Foreword

Colchester and its surroundings may not be the richest part of the country in terms of butterfly species, but what the area can justifiably boast about is its long tradition as a centre for the study of natural history. Not unconnected with this has been the remarkable ability to produce a string of first-rate naturalists, starting over 300 years ago with John Ray (1627-1705) who is widely acknowledged as the father of British natural history. The tradition continues today with the Field Studies Centre at Flatford Mill - admittedly just across the border in Suffolk but sporting a Colchester post-code - and a clutch of dedicated naturalists including the authors of this volume. Joe Firmln and Ted Benton have, between them, over 75 years of experience with Essex butterfiies. Joe is the long-serving Chairman of the Essex Lepidoptera Panel, while Ted is one of our foremost insect photographers, having captured some of the most beautiful and exciting butterfly images that I have ever seen. The pair are thus eminently well qualified to produce this book.

But, although its clear descriptions and superb photographs will allow readers to identify any butterfly that they might see in the area, this book does not pretend to be another field guide. It is a natural history of the butterflies of the region: a fascinating account of their lives, their history, and their future. Several of the species described are, sadly and for a variety of reasons, no longer with us in Essex. One should never say never again, especially with global warming already encouraging several continental species to move northwards, but widespread habitat destruction probably means that some butterflies have probably disappeared from Essex for ever. On the positive side, however, there are exciting plans to re-establish the purple emperor and the pearl-bordered fritillary in some of their former woodland homes. Hopefully, more species will join them in due course. And it is to the future that we must now look. After more than 100 years of decline, I hope the new millennium will bring an upturn in the fortunes of our butterflies. If, 300 years from now, it is still possible to write about the butterflies of the Colchester area, much of the credit will be due to the interest stimulated by the present book and to the work of today's naturalists.

Michael Chinery

Michael Chinery is author of Butterflies of Britain & Europe, A Photographic Guide (Harper Collins); Butterflies and Day-flying Moths of Britain & Europe (Collins) and the Collins Guide to the Insects of Britain & Western Europe. He is also President of the Cambridgeshire and Essex branch of Butterfly Conservation

Dedicated to the memory of Donald Blaxill and
Geoffrey A. Pyman, who devoted so much time to the
study and conservation of butterflies in Essex

ACKNOWLEDGEMENTS

The authors wish to express their thanks to Colchester Natural History Society, Colchester Borough Council and the John Ray Trust for financial support without which this book could not have been produced. We are also greatly indebted to the editorial committee of CNHS, B. Corben, P. Douch, I.C. Rose and D. Warner for invaluable editorial help and technical assistance and to Penelope Moores, who volunteered her experience as a proof reader. We also appreciate the support of J. Bowdrey, of Colchester Natural History Museum, the Local Studies staff of Colchester Library, and the Colchester branch of the Essex Record Office. I.C. Rose contributed the account of Weeley Woods in 'Where to Watch Butterflies', and also submitted butterfly records, as did C. Tyas and D. Urquhart.

Our thanks also go to the individual members of Colchester Natural History Society, whose active membership and conviviality have done so much to encourage us and others to continue our study of local wildlife.

The authors wish to place on record their particular appreciation of the preparation for printing of text and illustrations by Brian Corben, whose computer skills have ensured successful publication and also of the design, lay-out, art and style expertise of David Warner. Their combined talents have proved invaluable

INTRODUCTION

This book is written, first, for residents and visitors to North East Essex. Whether you are just beginning to take an interest in butterflies, or are an experienced 'butterfly-watcher' we hope there will be much to interest you. You will be able to identify any species that you are likely to see in our area by looking at the photographs, and then checking with the text for that species. Here you will find information about its life-history, the habitat, behaviour and distribution in the area. For beginners, our chapters on 'current residents' and migratory species will be very useful, narrowing down your search to only those species currently found here. For those who like to delve further, we have included chapters on the natural history and biology of butterflies ('Butterfly Lives'), and on the history of butterflies and butterfly-watching in our area ('The Lost Ones' and 'Butterfly-hunters'). We have tried to convey something of the historical continuity of love of nature and butterflies in particular, and we have tried to show how the changes in our local butterfly populations have been intertwined with our treatment of the environment we all share. If the chapter on 'The Lost Ones' is much longer than we would like, then we should learn from it in our current policies for transport, land use, forestry and urban development.

But we hope that our book will have an appeal beyond our local area. It does not pretend to cover all the British species, but it does cover nearly all those that are likely to be seen in most parts of lowland South East England, East Anglia, the Midlands and North. It does not include species confined to the more specialised habitats: chalk and limestone downlands, heaths, moors and mountains. For conservationists outside our area, we hope that our detailed accounts of the history of local butterfly populations will be of interest. The loss of so many woodland butterflies from North East Essex, and the decline of butterflies such as the grayling, grizzled and dingy skippers somewhat later, form part of a wider national pattern of decline and local extinction. If this decline is to be halted and reversed we need to understand its causes. In North East Essex we have a special contribution to make. In Victorian times our area was one of the richest butterfly-haunts in Britain and it also was well-endowed with expert naturalists whose collections, notebooks and publications give us an unrivalled insight into processes of environmental change and the associated fate of so many butterfly species. This book gathers together much of this information, a good deal of it not previously published, and never brought together in this form. Fortunately the tradition of the earlier naturalists has continued, with the maintenance of a thriving local natural history society (CNHS), and its commitment to local recording and regular publication.

For each species we give information about where it can be seen, and, in the case of the 'Lost Ones', give information about the nearest or most accessible places to see them outside our area. Some of the better-known and well-studied butterfly localities in North East Essex are listed, with details of species which occur there and how to get to them. There are, of course, many other places to see butterflies, and undoubtedly many that are unknown to current 'butterfly-buffs'. The real excitement is one of discovery:

and we hope this book will help you to make your own! Because our hope is to attract - even inspire! - beginners we have tried where possible to avoid using technical terms. However, sometimes there is reason to use 'jargon': it saves lengthy descriptions. To help with those technical terms we have used, a glossary is added. For stylistic reasons we sometimes use the more general scientific terms 'larva' and 'pupa' interchangeably with the more familiar terms (which apply to butterflies and moths only) 'caterpillar' and 'chrysalis'.

As editor of this publication it was easy for me to steal the opportunity of designing its front cover. The function of a book cover, apart from protecting its contents, is little different from that of a detergent pack, a wine label or a seed packet. It has to compete for your attention against the thousands of other publications that line the shelves of our bookshops. That is to say it must help to sell the book.

Montaging 15 close-up photographs of butterfly wings * with a large and symbolic question mark was an attempt to grab your attention. If you have read this far it has probably worked.

The inclusion of a question mark was not just a whimsical choice. The future of butterflies in this Country is questionable. The survival of their habitats is questionable. Whether or not your descendants will be able to walk through fields and woodland and enjoy the beauty of these creatures is questionable.

So when you see the fencing go up and the bulldozers preparing to go in, don't just ask questions. DO SOMETHING!

Editor.

*These were rescued from old collections (mostly over 50 years old), that were formed when, sadly, large series of identical butterflies were amassed purely for the pleasure of their owner, and for no scientific reason whatsoever.

Chapter 1   BUTTERFLY   LIVES

'Almost like two children together, I and this dark-eyed youth would chase the glorious Charaxes jasius, which occurred quite commonly on the arbutus-covered slopes of Gravitelli, quarrelling and disputing sometimes in hot discussions, while the music of the beautiful language in which we always conversed would add power and grace to our words. Then we would sit down and eat our luncheon beneath the shade of an olive tree, and it would seem as if the whole of nature's world, the flowers, the sunshine and the butterflies, were only made and created for us two, as we sat or lounged' (Fountaine 1982, p.89)

Perhaps not all butterfly-lovers have quite such romantic experiences as Margaret Fountaine, the intrepid Norwich adventurer. The butterfly collecting trip to Sicily, described above, took place in 1896, and marked the beginning of a life-long passion (in more senses than one) which took her through Europe, the middle east, Africa, India, Ceylon and the USA in search of rare and elusive butterflies. In those days, killing and collecting was the accepted method of study, though, interestingly, even then Fountaine did so with a sense of regret: '*It gave me a pang of remorse to take this beautiful creature away from her flowers and her sunshine, which I too knew so well how to enjoy; the death of the butterfly is the one drawback to an entymological* (sic) *career'* (*op.cit.* p.57).

Today, and for most purposes, careful observation of butterflies in their habitats, the notebook, camera and video recorder have largely replaced the killing bottle and setting board. The earlier generations of pioneering collectors, such as Margaret Fountaine, left us with a great store of knowledge which might not have been obtained in any other way, so that now we can carry on their work without the need to 'take these beautiful creatures away from their flowers and their sunshine'. Also, though some of us, like Fountaine, take great pleasure in travelling far and wide in search of butterflies, the growing interest in conservation makes us more concerned to know and to protect the familiar species: ones to be seen, almost literally, on our own doorstep. How much the poorer our lives would be without the anticipation of orange-tip butterflies along our spring hedgerows, or the occasional lucky glimpse of a tiny green hairstreak flying among bushes of broom. This book is devoted to these still-familiar, but seriously threatened 'other beings' whose existence so lightens our own lives.

Anatomy of a butterfly

The butterflies belong to a much bigger order of insects, the Lepidoptera (literally: scale-wings), which includes both butterflies and moths. On the global scale, there are no sharp distinctions between butterflies and moths, and most butterfly enthusiasts sooner or later extend their studies to the moths. However, in Britain, the butterflies are usually distinguished from moths by the shape of the antennae ('feelers'). These are widened towards the end to give a club-like appearance in butterflies, whilst the antennae of moths are variously shaped, often simple and thread-like, or feathery.

Usually moths rest with wings folded down over and beside their bodies, whilst butterflies close their wings up above their bodies. A less obvious characteristic is that moths have tiny 'hooks' linking fore- and hind-wings, which butterflies lack. Finally, butterflies are most active in the daytime, usually remaining at rest in the absence of sunshine, whilst most moths fly at dusk or during the night. However, there are some confusing exceptions to theses general points. The brightly coloured group of moths, the 'burnets', have thickened ends to their antennae and are day-flyers, and there are quite a few other common day-flying moths. The 'skipper' butterflies (well-represented in the Colchester district) have quite 'furry' bodies and look moth-like. Some writers, in fact, do not count them as butterflies.

Perhaps the reason why butterflies are so popular (apart from the fact that they don't sting or bite!) is the astonishing diversity of colour and patterning on their wings. As the scientific name of the order to which they belong suggests, these colours are produced by tiny scales which cover both surfaces of the wings like fine dust (which rubs off when a butterfly is worn with age or handled carelessly). In most cases, the colour-patterns are produced by the net effect of the mosaic of pigments on the scales, but in some species (especially the 'blues') iridescent colours are produced by the refraction of light through the scales. Relatively recently, scientific studies with ultra-violet light have shown quite distinctive patterns, probably important in butterfly 'courtship' and mating, which are not visible to the human eye. As well as playing their part in recognition for courtship and mating, wing colour-patterns may help provide camouflage for butterflies at rest (this is why the undersides are often so much less striking than the uppersides: think of the peacock and small tortoiseshell, for examples). They also in some cases distract predators from the vulnerable body of the butterfly. The vivid 'eye' markings of the peacock butterfly, on the outer tips of the wings, are a good example.

Adult butterflies have four wings, consisting, under the scales, of a thin, transparent membrane kept in shape by a framework of fine veins. These are usually visible even when covered with scales, and are useful points of reference when describing a butterfly's colour-pattern or wing-shape. Like most insects, the adult butterfly's body is divided into three distinct sections: head, thorax and abdomen. The butterflies' main sense-organs are situated on the head. Most evident are the large rounded compound eyes. These are composed of thousands of tiny individual facets which combine to form an image of the surroundings. These give relatively poor representations of shape, but are sensitive to movement, and especially to colours: in fact, butterflies are believed to be sensitive to a wider range of wavelengths of light than any other group of animals. There are also simple eyes, or 'ocelli', which are believed to be sensitive mainly to light and shade. The two antennae are organs of chemical sense - taste, scent and touch - and are used by females in detecting the appropriate plants for egg-laying, and sometimes used in 'courtship' displays. Below and in front of the eyes is a pair of furry 'palpi', also organs of chemical sense. Finally, between them, and tightly curled up when not in use, is the unique 'proboscis', or tongue. This is a very long double tube which the butterfly can unfurl and use to probe deep into flowers to reach their nectar store.

The chest or 'thorax' is made up of three fused segments. To it are attached the wings and the (usually) six, jointed legs. In flight, the wings perform a complex figure of eight pattern as they are flapped up and down. These actions are controlled indirectly by muscles which vary the shape of the hard outer 'skeleton' of the thorax. The abdomen is made up of ten joined segments. Along the sides, on each segment are tiny breathing-holes, or 'spiracles', and enclosed within the final segment are the sexual organs.

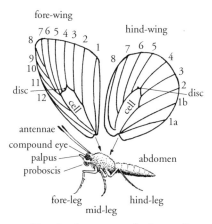

Fig. 1: Anatomy of a butterfly

Amazing transformations: life history
So far, we have described the adult butterfly only, but one of the most astonishing and fascinating aspects of the study of butterflies is their life-history. Each butterfly passes through four quite distinct stages during its life. First is the egg. This is tiny, and varies in shape according to the species concerned. Some, especially in the family of 'blue' butterflies (*Lycaenidae*), have exquisite patterns of sculpturing over their surfaces which can only be seen under high magnification. In some species the butterfly over-winters in the egg stage, but more usually the egg hatches after about a week (sometimes hatching can be predicted by a change in colour of the egg), and a tiny caterpillar ('larva') emerges. Often the first meal of the caterpillar is its own egg-shell. The newly-hatched caterpillar is totally unlike the butterfly it will (if lucky!) eventually become. It is tubular in shape, with a distinct head at the front end. The head carries the mouthparts, generally adapted for chewing plant material, and small antennae and ocelli. The rest of the body is usually quite soft and pliable, composed of 13 joined segments. There are six true legs, a pair on each of the first three segments, then, further back, several pairs of stubby 'pro-legs', and finally, a pair of claspers at the rear end (in some moth caterpillars - the 'loopers' - the pro-legs are absent). The caterpillar grows by periodically shedding its outer 'skin', in most species doing so four times before reaching its maximum size. The caterpillars of different species can usuall be

3

recognised by their distinctive shapes, colour patterns and by the hairs or, in some species, spiny projections, with which they are covered. This is complicated by the fact that in some species the colour pattern changes with the different stages (or 'instars') in the caterpillar's development. When full-grown, the caterpillar becomes less active, and spins a pad of silk threads (in some groups, such as the 'skippers', they construct a cocoon, as do many moth species). After a resting period, the 'skin' splits for the last time to reveal a new stage in the life-history: the chrysalis, or 'pupa'. The shapes of some of the features of the adult butterfly (eyes, antennae, legs, the abdominal segments and miniature wings) are embossed on the surface of the chrysalis, but it has no means of movement from place-to-place, being confined to the occasional sideways 'wiggle' of the abdomen. Though usually called a 'resting' stage, within the chrysalis the most amazing changes are taking place. As the chrysalis stage progresses, groups of unspecialised cells located in different parts of the former caterpillar's body begin to develop as organs of the adult butterfly. Eventually, even the colour pattern of the future butterfly can be seen through the tough outer coating of the chrysalis. Finally, this outer coating splits down the back, and the butterfly emerges. At this stage its wings are crumpled flaps which are gradually 'pumped up' by blood being forced through the veins until they achieve their characteristic shape. Soon the wings harden, and the butterfly flits off to find its first drink of nourishing nectar.

Hazards of the butterfly life

Beyond the female's careful selection of suitable places to lay her eggs, there is no parental care among the butterflies, and the vast majority of eggs laid never reach the adult stage. Many eggs are lost to animals which graze the plants on which they are laid, or die when managed grassland is cut. Caterpillars are consumed in great numbers by insectivorous birds. For example, a study carried out at the Institute of Terrestrial Ecology's Monks Wood, Cambridgeshire, showed that annual fluctuations in populations of the white admiral butterfly were mainly caused by birds taking mature caterpillars and pupae during the month of June. Up to 80% were lost from this single cause, less if warm weather enabled rapid development of the caterpillars. Over-wintering at various stages in the life-history is also a hazardous process, with risk of fungal and viral infections. In some species, again, there are huge losses to parasitic insects. These include parasitic 'wasps', especially those belonging to the family 'Ichneumonidae', and some groups of flies. These insects lay their eggs in the eggs or young caterpillars of their butterfly 'hosts'. When these hatch, the resulting grubs, or 'larvae' feed on the soft internal tissues of the unfortunate victim, avoiding the destruction of vital organs until they themselves are full-grown. At this point they become pupae, either within the caterpillar's 'skin', or in groups around the dead body of their 'host'. Sometimes, when butterflies are being bred in captivity, it can be a great disappointment to find that one's carefully tended caterpillars have been parasitised in this way. However, the parasites themselves have fascinating life-histories, and are well worthy of study in their own right.

So, with all these enemies, including ourselves, how do butterflies manage to survive at all? Parasites, of course, are dependent on leaving enough surviving members of the host species for their next generation to feed on: especially if they are specialised to attack only one species. It is now believed, for example, that the big fluctuations in numbers from year to year of the common blue butterfly of our urban gardens, the holly blue, are caused by its relationship to a specialised parasite. When the butterfly is common, the parasite finds its host easily and its numbers build up, so causing the butterfly to become more scarce. As this happens, the parasite, too, becomes more rare, and the butterfly population expands again. Caterpillars also have several means of defence from their enemies. Some are superbly camouflaged, with shape, colour and pattern often matching plant stems or the leaves on which they rest. The caterpillars of the orange tip and the purple emperor are excellent examples. Moth caterpillars can be even more versatile, some even managing to mimic a bird-dropping! Other caterpillars repel predators by their unpleasant taste, or by exuding nasty-smelling secretions. Some caterpillars, especially in the family of 'blues' (*Lycaenidae*), exude a sticky, sweet substance much appreciated by ants. It is believed that they may gain protection from parasites by their association with the ants. Yet another survival strategy is to feed together in large groups, giving the appearance of a single, much larger animal. Caterpillars of the small tortoiseshell, feeding on nettles, are a familiar example. Co-ordinated movements may also add to the protection by distracting a predator, and in some species the caterpillars tie protective sheaths of leaves around themselves with silk threads.

The adult butterflies are vulnerable to inclement weather, such as prolonged periods of cold, wet or windy conditions. However, they can often find a sheltered spot, either in the tree canopy or close to the ground in dense grasses, where they become inactive, thus conserving energy until better weather returns. A few species, such as the small tortoiseshell and comma, pass the winter in such a state, after building up their internal food stores in late summer and autumn. Insectivorous birds, small mammals, even frogs and toads often catch adult butterflies as well as caterpillars, and even quite large butterflies are often taken on the wing by 'hawker' dragonflies, such as the southern hawker (*Aeshna cyanea*) and emperor (*Anax imperator*). Various species of wasps and robber-flies also prey upon adult butterflies. An especially sinister enemy of adult butterflies are spiders, notably *Misumena vatia*, a common 'crab' spider which lies in wait on flower-heads, pouncing on butterflies as they alight to sip nectar.

Adult butterflies lack 'offensive weapons' in the form of stings or bites, but as we saw above, the colour patterns on the wings are sometimes arranged so as to divert predatory attacks away from the vulnerable body of the insect. The sudden display of the very large and bright 'eye' markings on the wings of the peacock butterfly have been shown to startle a would-be predatory bird sufficiently to allow the butterfly to escape (Tinbergen, cited in Whalley, 1980). The apparently haphazard flight of some species, with sudden, unpredictable changes of direction, probably also serves to out-manoeuvre and confuse predators. Other species, such as the adults of *Nymphalids* (including the red admiral, purple emperor and peacock butterflies) have powerful, rapid flight which enables them to evade capture on the wing. Finally, even very brightly coloured species often have cryptic under-sides which match their surroundings when they are at rest.

Butterfly behaviour

The behaviour of adult butterflies varies from species to species and there is much that amateur observers can do to add to our limited knowledge. Since butterflies are cold-blooded animals, their activity is largely controlled by their surrounding environment: especially by temperature and sunlight. Most species become inactive at night or in cool weather, but if alarmed some species will start a 'shivering' motion of the wings which raises the body temperature sufficiently for them to make a 'getaway' flight. Normally, however, they await the warmth and brightness of the sun to warm them up sufficiently for activity in the early morning or after a period of cool weather. To aid in this warming up process, butterflies often stretch out their wings so as to expose the maximum surface directly to the sun's rays. The dark colours, especially, absorb the heat energy, and this is carried to the insect's body by the circulation of blood from the wing-veins. One of us has observed a population of a Spanish species of 'blue' butterflies move at sunset over the brow of a hillside from the East-facing to the West-facing slope so as to be in position to catch the early morning sun. Other species of 'blue' butterflies which rarely open their wings in the heat of the day will do so in the very early morning after the chill of the night. In another, closely related species, the very dark coloration of the undersides, when correctly angled to the sun, absorbs enough heat for them to dispense entirely with open-winged 'basking'. In this country, some species which hibernate (such as small tortoiseshells, peacocks and commas - but not, interestingly, brimstones) spend much of their time early in the spring basking on light-coloured, reflective bare surfaces as a way of raising their body temperature.

After warming up sufficiently, most butterflies are immediately off in search of food. This is usually gained from sipping nectar from flowers with the extended proboscis. Often this activity is aided by a sort of 'pumping' action achieved by repeated slow raising and lowering of the wings as the insect feeds. Some experiments have shown that butterflies react differently to various colours at different times of day, but it is unclear why this is so. Most butterflies will feed from a wide variety of flowers, and useful research can be done observing which species they visit, how far they fly to find suitable food-sources, whether there is competition between members of the same species or between species for possession of 'choice' nectar-sources, and so on. In many species there are quite significant differences between males and females in the pattern of activity through the day. Males are often intensely involved in the pursuit of females, stopping only occasionally to feed at flowers. Females tend to be less active, feed at flowers more persistently, and, after mating, intermittently indulge in spells of egg-laying. However, there are many exceptions to this common pattern, and careful observation is worthwhile. In some species, notably the purple emperor and some 'blues', the insects will come down to feed on animal dung, or dead and rotting carcasses. In one wood in France many poplar admirals were observed to come down to feed from the squashed carcasses of slugs, killed by forestry vehicles. Such species, together with some 'whites' are also often to be seen drinking at wet or damp patches of soil, or at the edges of streams ('mud-puddling'). It is often assumed that this behaviour is prompted by dehydration on hot days, but since it is mainly males which act in this way it seems likely that they are also imbibing minerals important in the formation of sexually-attractant scents ('pheromones'). Some of the species which hibernate as adult insects are often to be seen feeding from ripe or rotting fruit (blackberries, plums, pears etc.) in late summer and autumn prior to their long winter fast.

As with other aspects of behaviour, the reproductive activities of butterflies show many interesting variations from species to species. In some, the males fly considerable distances in their persistent search for females, often stopping to get a closer look (and, presumably, smell) at any appropriately coloured object which comes into their field of view. Males of the large and small whites are familiar examples, as they fly close to the ground, investigating white flowers, scraps of white paper, etc., as they go. Commonly, species in which the males locate females in this way have widespread larval food-plants and so are not closely tied to a circumscribed territory. Other species (such as the marsh fritillary) have populations which are often limited to a small area where the larval food-plant grows, and this area is treated as a kind of group-territory. In yet other species the males establish an individual territory where they 'lurk', flying up only to confront intruding males or pursue passing females. Speckled wood males are a good example of this, generally choosing perches in sun-spots among shady woodland rides or lanes. Such territories are defended by behavioural 'threats', but rarely lead to serious conflict. Some species mark their territories with pheromones produced by glands on the male abdomen. The resulting scents may guide females to the male territory as well as indicate possession of the site to approaching males. Males of the large copper butterfly in continental Europe have been observed scent-marking a line of grass-stems leading from the patch of dock plants where the females were emerging to the male territories several tens of metres away.

When a male is lucky enough to approach a female his troubles may not be over. There is usually an initial courtship display (in some blues, for example, a rapid fluttering of the wings) during which pheromones are released from areas or discrete patches of 'scent-scales' on the male's wings. These scent-scales (or 'androconia') are often gathered together to form visible black markings on the wings. These are most obvious in the males of small, Essex and large skippers, wall brown, grayling and the larger fritillary butterflies, but are present in many others. If the female has already mated, she spreads her wings wide and raises her abdomen up towards the male. This posture looks quite provocative, and some observers mistake it for an invitation to the male. In fact it is a signal of rejection and the male eventually gives up trying to mate. When the female is freshly emerged and un-mated, she responds with a series of behavioural cues and the male moves round to her rear end and the pair mate back-to-back, attached at the tips of their abdomens. Sometimes the courtship sequence is very simple and rapid, but in other species it is complex and quite extended. In wood whites, for example, the pair face each other, and repeatedly 'doff' their antennae, flashing the white undersides to their tips. Subsequently their antennae are enclosed between the fore-wings of their partners, and they 'stroke' one another with extended probosces. In other species, courtship includes high, spiralling courtship flights. If undisturbed, mating may last for some hours. If disturbed, the pair will fly off together, though only one of them (the male in some species, the female in others) will do the actual flying, simply carrying its mate along with it.

Egg-laying females generally go about this activity more-or-less hidden in vegetation. In some species, such as the marbled white, the larvae feed on a variety of grasses and the females let their eggs drop freely among the food-plants. More usually, however, the females carefully search out the correct food-plant for the future caterpillars, and glue the eggs, one by one, or sometimes in large groups, on the plant tissue. Sometimes this may be on the underside of a leaf, sometimes at or close to a flower-bud, or in the fork of a twig. Surprisingly, however, some species do not lay their eggs on the food-plant at all, but in a carefully selected spot nearby. This is true of the silver-washed and pearl-bordered fritillaries, for example. The females of the former lay their eggs singly in cracks in the bark of trees, as much as four to five metres above ground level, leaving the newly hatched caterpillars to descend to the ground to find the violet plants on which they feed (see p.39). The caterpillars of most species are confined to feeding on just one, or a small number of closely related plants. This makes it particularly important that the females lay their eggs on or near a sufficient supply of the right plant species. They can often be observed carefully 'testing' plants with their feet and antennae before finally settling on an appropriate plant to receive their eggs. Whilst most caterpillars feed mainly on the leaves of their host-plant, some burrow into the highly nutritious flower-buds or seed-pods.

One of the most surprising and little-understood aspects of butterfly-behaviour is migration. The most well-known global example is the trans-continental journeying of the American milkweed butterfly, but several of our familiar British species also migrate. Some of these, such as the large white, have a locally resident population which is added to each year by migrants which come in across the Channel. Others, such as the painted lady migrate northwards from their strongholds in North Africa through Europe, producing new generations of butterflies as they do so. In every year at least some arrive in Britain, and in some 'invasion' years they do so in huge numbers. They carry on reproducing here through the summer, but are believed to die out by winter. This used to be true of the red admiral, but it is now reasonably well established that at least some manage to survive our winters. Other migrant visitors from continental Europe are less predictable in their appearance, but some of these, too, such as the clouded yellow, have their invasion years. Much rarer are the occasional 'vagrant' Camberwell beauty, Queen of Spain fritillary and pale clouded yellow. It could well be that with climate change some of these species will become established residents.

Butterfly-watching: methods

Nowadays butterfly-watching has become a popular activity, often as a result of bird-watchers switching to butterflies in the summer months. So much is unknown about the behaviour and habitat-needs of even common butterflies, that amateurs can make many valuable discoveries. Many of us make subjective judgements that butterflies are less common than they used to be. Whilst this is probably true, it is important to be able to give evidence for it, particularly if costly conservation measures are being suggested. A well-established method of counting butterflies is to choose a stretch of countryside which can be walked through on a regular basis. This can be divided into sections according to the habitats passed through on the walk: meadow, hedgerow, woodland etc. The aim is to repeat the walk on a regular basis (say once each week) through the season at a regular pace. Numbers of butterflies of each species observed within a standard distance (say three or five metres) either side of the route in each section of the walk can be counted. An effort should be made to do the walk under similar weather conditions each time. If this is continued throughout the season, it gives good information about the flight-periods of each species (their 'phenology'), and also about their different habitat preferences. If it is continued over a period of years, then it gives good evidence of fluctuations in the populations of each species. A variation on this method is to repeat the walk at hourly intervals during the day, to get an idea of the changes in the behaviour patterns of the different species at different times of day. For those of us with too many constraints on our time to do such systematic counting, there is still much to learn from direct observation of individual butterflies. They can be watched through binoculars without any disturbance to their activity. Sketches and written notes can be made of significant observations. Increasingly, butterfly-watchers make use of tape-recorders, the camera and video-recorder. This last, though expensive, is a very promising means for recording the more complicated sequences of interaction among butterflies, and between them and features of their environment.

Chapter 2   CURRENT RESIDENTS

SMALL SKIPPER   (*Thymelicus sylvestris*)   Plate 1

Description:

A small (wing-span approximately 30mm) orange-brown butterfly, with darkened wing-borders and variable darkening of the veins. Females are otherwise unmarked on the upper-sides, but the males have a prominent black band of scent-scales (androconia) set slightly diagonally across the fore-wings, tapering towards the hind margins of the wings at its inner end. The under-sides are pale orange-brown, with variable golden-greenish or greyish shading.

Similar Species:

See under Essex skipper.

Life History:

Small batches of pale yellow eggs are laid within the leaf-sheath of a tall grass-stem (usually Yorkshire fog (*Holcus lanatus*), but other grass species, such as false oat-grass (*Arrhenatherum elatius*) are sometimes used). When the caterpillars hatch they eat their egg-shells, but then hibernate in tiny silken cocoons in the sheath where the eggs were laid. They commence feeding on the blades of grass the following spring. The full-grown caterpillar has longitudinal pale and dark green stripes, and a green head. The chrysalis is also green, and is formed in a loose cocoon among grass-blades. The butterflies are on the wing throughout July, and into early August.

Habitat and Behaviour:

Rough, uncultivated grassy areas, with tufts of tall grasses, notably its main larval food-plant, Yorkshire fog, are the preferred habitat of this species. Like its close relative, the Essex skipper, it is common on sea walls and associated rough grassland, especially the remaining grazing marshes. It also occurs on road-side verges, in country parks, gardens, wide woodland rides, hedgerows, set-aside, ex-industrial sites and residual patches of 'waste land'.

The butterflies are on the wing a little earlier than the Essex skipper, but their flight periods overlap and they are often to be seen flying together. The males are territorial, maintaining their territories mainly by perching on prominent vegetation from which they fly up to intercept passing females. Both sexes bask among grasses, wings half-open in the sunshine, or nectar at the flowers of knapweed (*Centaureae nigra*), black horehound (*Ballota nigra*), creeping thistle (*Cirsium arvense*), and lesser burdock (*Arctium minus*). Observations by Pye et al. (2002, forthcoming) indicate knapweed as the favoured nectar source, though this will presumably vary with flowering times and local availability of different plant species.

Distribution and Status:
Historical-
Under the name *Hesperia thaumas*, Fitch (1891) declared it common throughout Essex, 'especially in the marshes'. According to Harwood (1903), it was abundant everywhere in rough, grassy places. Clark and Hobday (1966), reported it as common at Colchester, East Mersea, Little Clacton, Walton and Weeley. Subsequent authors (Firmin et al. 1975, Emmet and Pyman (1985) and Goodey and Firmin (1992) all affirm it to be still common and widespread.
Current-
The small skipper remains very common wherever there is suitable habitat in North East Essex. It may be seen at Cudmore Grove Country Park, East Mersea; Old Hall Marshes; the Markshall Estate, Coggeshall; meadows between Markshall and the village of Coggeshall; Hilly Fields, Colchester; the Roman River Valley; Holland Haven Country Park and in many other places. Like the Essex skipper, it has recently extended its range in Britain.

ESSEX SKIPPER   (*Thymelicus lineola*)   Plates 1, 2

Description:
The first specimens to be recognised as belonging to this species were caught in Essex: hence its popular name. A small species (wing span 27-30mm.), both sexes have bright orange brown upper-sides, with blackish wing-margins and variable darkening along the veins. The male has a fine black line of scent-scales (androconia) which runs from the middle of each fore-wing towards the wing-base, and nearly parallel to the lead-edge of the wing. The under-sides are paler orange-brown, with pale greenish or greyish areas on the hind-wings.

Similar Species:
The small skipper is very similar, so much so that it was not until 1889 that the two species were recognised as distinct. The line of scent-scales in the males is differently shaped, much more prominent in males of the small skipper, and placed more diagonally across the wing, tailing off towards the rear wing-margin at its inner-end. More generally used as a way of separating the two species is the coloration of the tips of the antennae. However, care is needed in using this feature. Some sources simply state that the Essex skipper can be recognised by the black tips to the antennae, but in fact small skippers also often have black-tipped antennae, especially on the upper-sides. To be sure of your identification, the antennae should be viewed from the front and below. In the Essex skipper they look as though they have been dipped in black ink: that is, there is a sharp transition from the orange ground-colour to the black tip. In the small skipper, the tips are also often darkened, and may be black, but the transition is much more gradual. There are also slight differences in behaviour, habitat and flight period which can provide helpful initial clues.

11

Life History:
This was first described in this country by its discoverer, F.W. Hawes in *The Entomologist* (1892). The white eggs are laid in a row in flower-sheaths of coarse grasses. Cock's-foot (*Dactylis glomerata*) is reputed to be the main food-plant of the caterpillars, but Pye et al. observed egg-laying on false oat-grass (*Arrhenatherum elatius*) and Timothy (*Phleum pratense*), and they may use a variety of other species. They spend the winter in this stage. The caterpillars hatch in the spring and feed on grass blades through April, May and June. They have longitudinal dark and pale green stripes, and enclose themselves in tubes made by fastening together the edges of a grass blade with silk threads. The chrysalis is also green, and enclosed within a 'tent' made of grass blades. The butterflies emerge in July, a little later than the small skipper.

Habitat and Behaviour:
The Essex skipper is particularly common on the rough grassy areas around the coasts and estuaries of North East Essex, and on remaining grazing-marshes. But it is also to be found inland in many places where the common coarse grasses, upon which the caterpillars feed, grow. Such places include country parks and lightly managed public open spaces, roadside verges, hedge-margins, open woodland rides and ex-industrial sites in urban areas.

The flight of the males is typical of the 'skippers': fast and direct. They often 'bask', wings half-open, among tall grasses on sunny days, and can be seen nectaring, often in large numbers, on flowers such as black horehound (*Ballota nigra*), knapweed (*Centaurea nigra*), red clover (*Trifolium pratense*) and various thistles. As with the small skipper, it seems that preference for long narrowly tubular flowers or florets is connected with the long tongues (probosces) of both species, each with a 90 degree bend (see photograph, plate 2). As with the small skipper, males are territorial, often engaging in spiralling territorial combat flights with other males, and also patrolling in search of females (*Pye et al., 2002, forthcoming*).

Distribution:
Historical-
The species was first separated from the small skipper by F.W. Hawes, on the basis of three males caught in Hartley Wood, St. Osyth, in July 1888, which he compared with plates in Lang's *Rhopalocera Europeae*. Subsequent field work and the examination of existing collections soon established that the species was quite widespread, Mathew reporting it from Harwich and F.G. Whittle noting its occurrence on the marshes near Purfleet. Spiller had found it plentiful around Stansted between 1885-8, but had not seen it there between 1874 and 1876 when he had previously lived in the area. Harwood reported it as common all along the coast, but as apparently not to be found far inland. An account in Vol 7 of the *Essex Naturalist* (anon. 1893, pp.67/8) reported the sea walls as its 'partiality', where it sat on coarse grasses, or on the blossoms of thistle or bird's-foot trefoil. Subsequent reports continue to associate it with coastal localities. (*Hawes 1890, Mathew 1892, Hawes 1892, Spiller 1890, Harwood 1903*).

Current-
Common and widely distributed in rough, unmanaged grassy areas throughout our area. Asher et al. (2001) record its rapid expansion in recent decades, including in its current range all of South Eastern England and East Anglia, with new discoveries in the south west, and as far north as Yorkshire.

LARGE SKIPPER (*Ochlodes venata*)   Plate 2

Description:
As its name suggests, this is the largest butterfly of the 'skipper' family in our area (wing-span 33-35 mm.). The ground-colour of the upper-side is orange-brown, but with wide darker borders to the wings, broken by squarish orange-brown spots. The males have a strong black band of scent-scales running diagonally across the fore-wings. The under-side hind-wings are yellowish to olive green, with a row of inconspicuous paler spots, and an orange-brown area towards the inner edge. The under-side fore-wings have a pattern similar to that on the upper-side but with olive-green towards the wing-tips.

Similar Species:
The dark, broken borders to the upper-sides distinguish this species from both the small and Essex skippers. When the pale markings on the under-side are strongly contrasting, there is a close resemblance to the silver-spotted skipper. However, this is a chalk and limestone down land species which does not occur in Essex. The Lulworth skipper could also be confused with the large skipper, but it, too, does not occur in our district.

Life History:
The butterfly has a long flight period, and can be seen from the end of May, through June and July and into August. The dome-shaped white eggs are laid singly on blades of grass - usually cock's foot (*Dactylis glomerata*). The caterpillars are green, with a darker green line down the back and a pale stripe along each side. They live in a shelter made by binding the edges of a grass blade together with silk threads, and feed on grass blades. The winter is spent in the caterpillar stage, and feeding is resumed in the spring. The chrysalis is formed in a silk cocoon on a grass blade.

Habitat and Behaviour:
A very wide range of habitats is used, such as rough grassland in country parks, overgrown ex-industrial sites, river-banks, woodland rides, sea walls and adjacent grazing marshes, wide roadside verges, churchyards, hedgerows and unmanaged allotments. The coarse grass on which the caterpillars feed is very common and widespread, but the butterfly needs relatively un-managed sites, with areas or fringes of grass left uncut. The males often 'sit', wings half-open, on a prominent perch, flying up to intercept

passing females. They can also adopt a 'patrolling' method of locating mates. Both males and females can often be seen taking nectar from flowers.

Distribution and Status:
This butterfly remains very common and widespread in our area and can be seen wherever suitable rough grassy habitats can be found.

BRIMSTONE   (*Gonepteryx rhamni*)   Plate 3

Description:
With an average wing-span of 60mm., this is a fairly large species. The fore-wings curve to a point at their tips, and there is a similar projecting 'tail' to the hind -wings. The ground colour of the males is a bright sulphur yellow on the upper-side, with a small orange spot on each wing. The females are a much paler whitish green, but also have the orange spots. The male under-side is shaded green on the hind-wings and the outer portion of the fore-wings. As with the upper-side, the female under-side is much paler. In both sexes the veins on the under-side of the hind-wings are noticeably paler than the rest of the wings.

Similar Species:
No other species likely to be seen in Britain is similar to the brimstone. The clouded and pale clouded yellows are smaller, have a more rapid flight, and are strongly marked with black. The wing-shape of the brimstone, too, is quite distinctive.

Life History:
This is the only member of the 'white' family which over-winters as an adult insect. In the Autumn they seek out suitable places to hibernate, often among ivy or holly, where their wing shape and colour gives excellent camouflage. They are among the earliest butterflies to be seen in the Spring. Harwood (1903) reported seeing one in High Woods, Colchester on Christmas Day! The larval food-plants are buckthorn (*Rhamnus cathartica*) and alder buckthorn (*Frangula alnus*). The eggs are whitish and flask-shaped, laid singly towards the tips of the twigs on bushes of the food-plants during the Spring. The caterpillars are blue-green with a pale stripe down each side, and they rest along the mid-rib of a leaf. The chrysalis is green, and hatches in early to mid August. The adult butterflies feed actively from flowers and soon find a place to hibernate - usually among the leaves of evergreens such as holly and ivy.

Habitat and Behaviour:
Where the larval food plants are common, brimstones may be seen in large numbers, especially shortly after their emergence in August. This is true of the rides in some of the woods and green-lanes of North-west Essex, on the chalk, where buckthorn (*Rhamnus cathartica*) is common. After hibernation in the spring they tend to disperse

through the countryside.

Distribution and Status:

Both larval food-plants are scarce in North East Essex (Tarpey and Heath 1990, p. 110), and brimstones are usually seen singly as they fly on in search of mates or food-plants in the Spring. Numbers vary considerably from year to year, and there must be some doubt whether we have a consistent breeding population in our part of the county. The best chance of seeing brimstones is in woodland in early Spring, or again in August. High Woods, Colchester; Broakes Wood, Halstead; Chalkney Wood, Earls Colne and Markshall, Coggeshall are among the places where it is seen fairly regularly.

LARGE WHITE   (*Pieris brassicae*)   Plate 3

Description:

This is the largest butterfly in the 'white' family, with wing-spans up to 70mm. The ground colour of the upper-sides is a brilliant white, with black markings. Both sexes have an un-broken black tip to the fore-wings, whilst females have additional black markings on the fore-wings, and may also have more creamy or yellowish white hind-wings. The markings consist of two black spots, and a wedge-shaped band along the rear edge of the wing. There is also a small black triangular spot on the leading edge of the hind wing in both sexes, but this is usually obscured by the fore-wing in living specimens. The under-side hind-wings and the tips of the fore-wings are pale yellow or greenish grey, with a variable light dusting of darker scales. The black spots in the female are also present on the under-side. In the spring brood, the black markings are more greyish, giving a less contrasting appearance.

Similar Species:

Female brimstones are pale in colour and approximate to large whites in size, but wing-shape and the lack of black markings are distinctive. Confusion with other species of white butterflies is possible. However, both small and green-veined whites are usually noticeably smaller, and are weaker fliers. The green venation, especially on the under-sides of the green-veined white is distinctive. Small whites, especially females in the summer brood, are less easy to distinguish. However, the males have a central spot in the fore-wing, absent in the large white. In females, the pattern of spots is similar in both species, but the spots, and especially the wing-tips, are much more faintly marked in the small white. The ground colour of the wings is also a more creamy white than that of the large white, and is pale yellow in some specimens.

Life History:

This species was once regarded as a serious pest of cultivated Brassicas, hence its popular name, 'cabbage white'. The eggs may be laid on a number of both cultivated and wild members of the family Cruciferae, but cultivated cabbage and Brussels sprouts (*Brassica oleracea*) are favoured. Oil-seed rape (*Brassica napus*) and nasturtium (*Tropaeolum majus*). The eggs, which are yellow and flask-shaped are laid in clusters, usually on the under-side of a leaf of the larval food-plant. The fully grown caterpillars are green with a pattern of black markings and a yellow line down the back. When present in large numbers they strip off the foliage of the food-plant and are unmistakable. The caterpillars are very vulnerable to a parasitic wasp (*Apanteles glomeratus*) whose larvae feed on its body-contents, emerging when the caterpillar is full-grown. The tiny yellow cocoons of the wasp pupae can often be seen clustered round the dead body of their former 'host'. Un-parasitised caterpillars attach themselves to a solid surface such as a window-sill or crevice in a wall by way of a silken thread around the middle and pupate. The chrysalis is pale grey-green with small black markings, and is rather angular in shape. The winter is spent in the chrysalis stage. The adult butterfly has two, sometimes three flight periods in the year. The first begins in April, and continues through May into June; the second is in August, and the third, when it occurs, is in September and October. The resident population is regularly boosted by migrants from continental Europe, with occasional years of mass migration.

Habitat and Behaviour:
The familiar 'cabbage white' favours fields, gardens and allotments where its larval food-plants are cultivated. The adults do not have a defined territory, but fly considerable distances, in the case of males seeking mates, and in the case of females seeking out suitable plants on which to lay their eggs. The males tend to be much more active, and have a powerful flight. Both sexes stop to nectar at a variety of wild and cultivated flowers, the spring brood favouring dandelions (*Taraxacum spp.*), and the summer brood being very partial to buddleia (*Buddleia davidii*) in gardens. The males usually nectar with wings closed, but bask with wings open in early morning and late afternoon on sunny days.

Distribution and Status:
Fitch (1891) referred to it as 'too common everywhere', and this must have been the general view, given its preference for cultivated brassicas until the use of pesticides became widespread on farms and gardens. Although it remains a common and widespread butterfly, its populations must have been drastically reduced by new agricultural methods.

SMALL WHITE (*Pieris rapae*) Plate 4

Description:
As its name suggests, this is a relatively small species (average wing-span 48mm.). The upper-sides are pale creamy-white, with darkened tips to the fore-wings, and dark grey-black spots. In the males there is just one spot on the fore-wing, and another on the leading edge of the hind-wing (usually obscured by the over-lapping fore-wing in

living specimens). Females have two spots on each fore-wing, and a darkened area on the hind-edge of the fore-wing. In the later generations, both sexes are more strongly marked with black, but the ground-colour, too, is often more creamy or even yellowish (especially in the females). On the under-side, the hind-wing and the area around the apex of the fore-wing are yellow. The remainder of the under-side fore-wing is white, with the same pattern of black spots as on the upper-side. The under-side of the hind-wing is variably dusted with darker scales.

Similar Species:
In continental Europe there are two very similar species, the mountain small white (*P. ergane*) and southern small white (*P. mannii*). However, there is no likelihood of meeting with either of these in our area! See pp.15 &18 for differences between the small white and the large and green-veined whites.

Life History:
The yellow flask-shaped eggs are laid on the leaves of one of the larval food-plants. Like the large white, this species also makes use of cultivated plants, such as cabbage and nasturtium, but in addition it may lay its eggs on a range of wild crucifers. These include wild cabbage (*Brassica oleracea*), charlock (*Sinapis arvensis*), hedge mustard (*Sisymbrium officinale*) and garlic mustard (*Alliaria petiolata*). Hoary cress (*Cardaria draba*) is particularly favoured in coastal sites. The caterpillars are pale green and well-camouflaged. The pupae are also green, with yellow points, and may be attached to the food-plant, or to the surface of a fence or wall. The first generation of adults can be seen from late April, becoming more common in May and continuing to June. There is usually one, sometimes two subsequent generations in the season. The winter is spent in the pupal stage, a warm spring enabling early emergence.

Habitat and Behaviour:
Like the large white, this species has no defined territory, and the adults fly over rough grassland, along lanes, through gardens or along sea walls. The males investigate white objects and patches of the food-plant, presumably in search of females, whilst the female can often be observed flying from plant to plant laying eggs she goes. Both sexes take nectar from a wide range of flowers, though the summer brood is especially partial to thistles and knapweed (*Centaurea nigra*). In spring dandelions (*Taraxacum spp.*) are a popular source of nectar. Both sexes bask with wings open early in the day and in late afternoon, but are otherwise quite difficult to approach for photography.

Distribution and Status:
Though its populations must have been much affected by the use of chemical insecticides on cultivated Cruciferae, it remains a very common and widespread butterfly. As with the large white, the resident population is swelled by an annual immigration from continental Europe.

GREEN-VEINED WHITE *(Pieris napi)* Plate 4

Description:
This butterfly is similar in size to the small white (average wing-span 50mm.). The ground-colour of the upper-side is a brilliant white (especially in the males), with variable dark grey to black markings. The fore-wing tips and around the outer-edge of the fore-wings are marked with grey-black, which often also extends into the wing along the veins. The males have a single black spot in the fore-wing, well-marked in the summer brood, but faint and sometimes absent in the spring. The females have two black spots in the fore-wing, linked to dark shading along the rear edge. The wings of the females are often partly suffused with darker scaling, especially along the wing-veins. The hind-wings are unmarked except for a small black mark on the leading edge (sometimes missing in spring males). The under-sides are very striking. The ground colour is yellow on the hind-wing, and around the apex of the fore-wing, with dark grey-green edging to the veins. This is less extensive in the summer brood.

Similar Species:
For distinction from small and large whites see pp.15 & 16. In continental Europe there are numerous forms of green-veined white, and how to classify them is still a matter of dispute. However, this is not a problem in our district: the green outlining of the veins on the under-side is quite unmistakable.

Life History:
The flask-shaped pale yellow eggs are laid singly on the leaves of the larval food-plants. These are usually wild members of the Cruciferae, including hedge mustard *(Sisymbrium officinale)*, garlic mustard *(Alliaria petiolata)* and cuckooflower *(Cardamine pratensis)*. The caterpillars are dark green with yellow rings round the spiracles at the side of each segment. The pupae vary in colour from green to brown, and the insect over-winters in this stage. There are usually two generations each year, with a third brood in favourable years. The first generation flies early in the year, sometimes as early as the beginning of April, but they are more common in May and early June, by which time the offspring of those flying in early spring may already be on the wing. Subsequent generations may be seen flying through the summer and into September.

Habitat and Behaviour:
Although individuals of this species may be seen flying well away from their breeding-sites, they are generally less mobile than their relatives, the large and small whites. They are most likely to be found along hedge-rows, damp seepages from lakes and ponds, stream-sides and damp corners in meadows or woodland rides where their larval food-plants grow. They tend to share these habitats with the orange tip, and the two species often fly together in our district. The males spend much of their time actively 'patrolling' in search of females, investigating white flower-heads, or even fragments of
18

white litter. Like other whites, they are also frequently seen basking with wings wide open, especially in early morning, late afternoon or following periods of cloud-cover. They are more easily approached when basking than other whites.

Distribution and Status:
Early accounts agree on its general abundance, and it remains a very common and widespread butterfly. It has almost certainly lost many suitable habitats to land-drainage, building and agricultural intensification. However, since it is not dependent on cultivated Cruciferae, it has not suffered directly from the use of chemical insecticides as have large and small whites. It seems able to sustain populations on quite small areas of suitable habitat, presumably with considerable interchange between local populations. Its main food-plants remain very common throughout North East Essex.

ORANGE-TIP *(Anthocharis cardamines)*   Plate 5

Description:
In size the orange-tip is usually similar to the small and green-veined whites, but much smaller specimens sometimes occur. Both sexes are pure white on the upper-sides, with a black discal spot and unbroken black shading of the tip in the fore-wing. Males are distinguished by a bright orange patch towards the tip on the fore-wing, absent in the females. The under-side hind-wings have a complex pattern of white with green mottling, whilst the males have a repeat of the upper-side orange patch on the under-side fore-wings.
There is a very rare colour-variation of the males *(ab. aureoflavescens* Cockerell), which have the orange patches replaced by yellow. Harwood (1903) reported having bred a specimen of this form in 1899, and another was captured by J. Firmin in Friday Wood on May18th 1958.

Similar Species:
The males are unlikely to be confused with any other species occurring in Britain. The females could be confused with other whites, but the under-side pattern is quite distinctive, even when compared to well-marked green-veined whites. There is one species, common in much of Europe, but a very rare migrant in Britain, with which the female orange-tip could be confused. This is the so-called 'Bath white' *(Pontia daplidice)*, and it is more heavily marked with black on the upper-sides than is the female orange-tip. Also, the black markings around the wing-tips are broken, and the under-side green mottling is more even and regularly distributed.

Life History:
The eggs are laid singly at the base of the flower-heads of the larval food-plants, which in our area are usually cuckooflower *(Cardamine pratensis)* or garlic mustard *(Alliaria*

19

petiolata). The eggs soon turn orange in colour and are quite easy to find. It is reported that the females secrete a hormone which deters other females from laying on the same flower, and females can be observed flying up to plants of cuckooflower, as if to lay an egg, but quickly flying on. Subsequent observation commonly reveals that there is already an egg on the plant. It seems that there is only enough nutrition in a plant of cuckoo flower to feed a single larva, and if more larvae are present they are cannibalistic. These adaptations suggest that cuckoo flower may have been the original food-plant of this species, since plants of garlic mustard would appear to be capable of sustaining more than one larva. The caterpillars are long and thin, pale blue-green above and darker green underneath, and they feed on the developing seeds of the food-plant. Like the caterpillars, the pupae are very well camouflaged. They are usually straw-coloured and angular-triangular in shape, closely resembling a dead plant-stem. The winter is spent in the chrysalis stage, and the butterflies begin to emerge in April. They are more common in May and early June, but in some years can be seen as late as July. Rarely, there is a small second generation.

Habitat and Behaviour:
Like other species of 'whites', the butterflies range widely over the country-side, and the males are especially noticeable as they fly along lanes or hedge-rows in search of females. However, they are more often seen at their breeding sites, which include damp areas in meadows, the edges of ditches and streams, and damp woodland rides, as well as hedge-rows and road-side verges - wherever their larval food-plants grow. They often fly together with the first generation of the green-veined white, and share the same species of larval food-plants. However, they do not directly compete, as their caterpillars feed on the young seeds, whilst those of the green-veined white feed on the leaves. In cloudy weather, the adult butterflies settle, wings closed, on low-growing vegetation, often flower-heads of Umbelliferae, such as cow parsley (*Anthriscus sylvestris*), on which they are beautifully camouflaged. In sunny weather both sexes nectar or bask, wings partly open, on flower-heads of such plants as cuckooflower and bluebell (*Hyacinthoides non-scripta*).

Distribution and Status:
Earlier writers, such as Fitch (1891) and Harwood (1903) concur in assessing it as a plentiful and widespread species in Essex. Despite considerable habitat changes in the intervening period it remains remarkably widespread and even common in North East Essex, though it is never seen in large numbers.

GREEN HAIRSTREAK (*Callophrys rubi*) Plate 5

Description:
A small species (average wingspan 33mm.). The upper-sides of the wings in both sexes are uniform dark brown, fading in older specimens. At rest the butterfly always closes

its wings, so only the under-sides are visible. These are bright green, with a variable line of white spots (the 'hairstreak') across the wings. Sometimes this is reduced to just a few white specks on the hind wings. There is a very fine reddish fringe to the wings, which also extends along the leading edge of the fore-wing, and there is a distinctive white rim around the eyes.

Similar Species:
In flight the green hairstreak might be mistaken for another of the small brown butterflies (perhaps a dingy skipper or a female common blue). However, once seen at rest its bright green under-side is quite unmistakable. Only the rare southern European Chapman's green hairstreak resembles it - an unlikely find in North East Essex!

Life History:
The adults fly in spring, sometimes as early as the first week in April, and on through May into early June. The females lay their pale green eggs singly on leaves and buds at the tips of young shoots of the larval food plants. These include bird's-foot trefoil (*Lotus corniculatus*), dyer's greenweed (*Genista tinctoria*), dogwood (*Cornus sanguinea*) and buckthorn (*Rhamnus catharticus*), but in our area broom (*Cytisus scoparius*), and sometimes gorse (*Ulex europaeus*), seem to be preferred. The caterpillar feeds on the buds and flowers of the shrubs on which the eggs were laid, and when full-grown is green, with yellow markings along its body. The chrysalis is said to be dark brown, and attended by ants. The insect hibernates as a chrysalis.

Habitat and Behaviour:
In our area, the green hairstreak is to be found in scrubby heathland with gorse and broom, railway cuttings, old sand and gravel pits, open areas in woods, hedgerows and gardens. The males are strongly territorial and settle on vantage points, sometimes on well-established bushes of broom, or on overlooking trees. From these perches they fly out to engage other males in often very prolonged zig-zag territorial 'combat' flights, or to intercept females. The females are most often seen while investigating young shoots of the larval food-plants prior to egg-laying. They rarely, if ever, open their wings except to fly, and so can be very difficult to spot when settled among green shoots and pods of broom.

Distribution and Status:
Historical-
Jermyn (1827) gave Bromley Thicks as a location to find this species. Fitch (1891) reported it as 'not common' but widely distributed in Essex. Harwood (1903) commented that it was common and generally distributed in 'rough places where broom and furze grow freely'. Firmin et al. (1975) reported that it remained widespread, and was often common where its habitat remained intact, and a similar impression is given in Emmet and Pyman (1985). Referring specifically to North East Essex, Goodey and Firmin (1992) give its status as local and 'frequent' (i.e. 5-15 seen

annually), but report that it became 'fairly numerous' in 1991 at Friday Wood.
Current-
It seems very likely that building development (e.g. the building of student
accommodation on the University of Essex campus), changed forestry practice and
more intensive agriculture have combined to greatly reduce available habitats for this
species. However, significant areas of habitat remain, such as in EWT reserves, on
M.o.D. land, in some coastal areas and in urban and suburban gardens. Where there is
suitable habitat it can still be found in fair numbers, and in some years is abundant.
Despite its distinctive colouration the butterfly is easily over-looked, and is likely to
have been under-recorded. It retains strong colonies in such places as the M.o.D.
heathland around Friday Wood, Fingringhoe Wick Nature Reserve, Copt Hall
(National Trust, Little Wigborough), Hilly Fields (Colchester), Old Hall Marsh
RSPB Reserve, Cudmore Grove Country Park (East Mersea), and Langenhoe. It has
recently shown signs of colonising new sites, and has been recorded in Colchester town
centre gardens, presumably using dogwood as its larval food-plant.

PURPLE HAIRSTREAK *(Neozephyrus (Quercusia) quercus)*   Plate 5, 6

Description:
This species is slightly larger than the green and white-letter hairstreaks, with a wing-
span of 37-39mm. The upper-side ground-colour in both sexes is black, with a purple
sheen. In the males the purple covers most of the wing-surface, except for the margins,
but is only visible when viewed from certain angles. In the females, the purple is
confined to the cell area, and an area along the hind margin of the fore-wing. The
under-side is silvery grey with a clearly defined white 'hairstreak' across both fore- and
hind-wings. There is a small 'tail' projecting form the hind edge of the hind wings,
and a black-centred orange spot close to it.

Similar Species:
At a distance it might be possible to mistake the purple and white-letter hairstreaks for
one another. However, if good views are obtained, the dark upper-sides and silvery
grey under-sides are quite distinctive.

Life History:
The grey, disc-shaped eggs are laid on oak *(Quercus spp.)* twigs or buds. These may be
anywhere on the canopy, but are often laid quite close to the ground, and on scrub-oaks,
where they are easily found. The caterpillars do not hatch until the following spring,
when they begin feeding on the oak buds, and later on the leaves. They are brown in
colour, and feed at night. The pupa is reddish brown, and reported to be taken into
ants' nests underground.

Habitat and Behaviour:
Populations of this butterfly fluctuate greatly from year to year, as the historical account below suggests. It is also easily overlooked, especially where it occurs in dense, mature woodland. It seems likely that it is more widespread than current records suggest. Most of our larger woods, and many smaller woods, copses and stands of oak probably harbour colonies of the purple hairstreak. The adults fly in the latter part of July and well into August. They can often be seen flying erratically around the canopy of oak trees, and are best observed on sapling or scrub-oaks, when they will often come down to eye-level. Much of their time is spent settled on the foliage or flitting round the contours of branches. Usually in the heat of the day they settle with wings closed, but especially early in the morning, or during bright spells on cloudy days, they open their wings to reveal their purple sheen. They can sometimes be observed sucking up honeydew left by aphids on oak leaves, or, less commonly, taking nectar from bramble blossom or 'mud-puddling' from damp paths.

Distribution and Status:
Historical-
Jermyn gave Ramsey, Wrabness and Bromley Thickets as Essex localities whilst Fitch regarded it as common in most woods, where it was partial to ash stubs, settling on leaves and sheltering under them in dull weather. According to Harwood it was common and generally distributed in oak woods. Friedlein reported 'countless' purple hairstreaks at a locality near North Fambridge (July 29th), and also noted their 'abundance' at a wood on the river Stour, in the North East of Essex (1st. August), both observations in 1951. Subsequently, Friedlein noted the local decline of woodland butterflies, the purple hairstreak (among other species) being 'almost extinct'. Clark and Hobday, reporting a 1963 survey, gave North East Essex localities as Colchester and Fingringhoe. Firmin et al. report the species as widely distributed in woods, but also in little-wooded areas such as Bradwell-on-Sea. 'Reasonable numbers' were present in the woods round Colchester, and the butterfly much more in evidence in the fine summers of 1970 and 1971. Emmet and Pyman, whilst stating that the species was usually much less common than formerly, note its greater numbers in the hot, dry summers of 1976, 1983 and 1984. Goodey and Firmin refer to it as still widespread and common in the North East of the county at the beginning of the 1990s.
(Jermyn 1827, Fitch 1891, Friedlein 1956, Friedlein - note in Essex Naturalist 1966, p. 157, Clark & Hobday 1966, Firmin et al. 1975, Emmet & Pyman 1985, Goodey & Firmin 1992)
Current-
The butterfly may have lost some of its former habitat through changes in woodland management, but it remains widespread throughout our district wherever suitable habitat remains. Current localities include: Hillhouse Wood, West Bergholt; Friday Wood, Donyland Wood and the other woodlands along the Roman River valley; the Markshall woodlands, Coggeshall; Pods Wood, Tiptree; Broak's Wood, Gosfield; Weeleyhall Wood and Wivenhoe Wood. The butterfly is also often found on oaks in

non-woodland habitat, such as along the edge of Hilly Fields and Lexden Springs Local Nature Reserve, Colchester, and on the old oaks on the campus of Essex University.

WHITE-LETTER HAIRSTREAK   (*Satyrium w-album*)   Plate 6

Description:

Another small species (wing-span approx. 36mm.). When not in flight, the white-letter hairstreak keeps its wings closed. So, only the under-side is visible. The ground colour is medium to dark brown, with a white 'streak' across both fore- and hind-wings, making the shape of a 'W' on the hind-wing. There is a band of orange lunules close to the edge of the hind-wings and a projecting 'tail' to the hind-edge of the hind-wing. This is usually longer in the females. The upper-sides of the wings are a uniform blackish brown, with a variable small orange spot in the rear corner of each hind-wing.

Life History:

Owing to the threat posed by the spread of Dutch elm disease, the life history of this butterfly has been thoroughly researched. The females lay their eggs singly on buds or twigs of elm trees. Wych elm (*Ulmus glabra*) is reputed to be preferred, but larvae will also feed on English elm (*U. procera*) and small-leaved elm (*U. minor*). The eggs are pale green in colour at first, but later turn grey and are well camouflaged. The butterfly over-winters at this stage, and the young larvae hatch in early spring. Normally, they begin to feed on expanding flower-buds, then leaf-buds and subsequently on the elm leaves. The full-grown caterpillar is pale green with darker-green markings which resemble the veins on an elm leaf. The chrysalis is dark brown and hairy, often attached to an elm twig by a silk thread. The butterflies usually emerge in early July and continue to fly on into August. It was believed that the flower-buds were essential to the nutrition of the young larvae, and so Dutch elm disease might devastate populations of this butterfly. In fact, the disease did lead to a drastic decline, and a WWF project was set up in the 1980s to research the butterfly and suggest conservation measures. The butterflies have survived in many places on sucker re-growth from the base of dead trees. Since these are vulnerable to re-infection when they begin to flower, survival of the butterfly depended on the caterpillars' being able to dispense with the flower-buds as an early nutritional source. It has now been shown that, indeed, they are able to survive on non-flowering elm suckers. (*C. Steel 1984, Oates 1984, M. Davies 1986, M. Davies 1992*)

Habitat and Behaviour:

Formerly the white-letter hairstreak was considered primarily a woodland species preferring mature elms growing along rides or along woodland edges. However, it has also frequented elms growing in sheltered hedgerows, elms growing in urban and suburban streets, and isolated trees. Prior to the onset of Dutch elm disease, it seems likely that the butterfly was under-recorded in many places because of its tendency to

24

remain high in the canopy of tall trees. There it feeds on aphid 'honeydew' on leaves, and can often be observed flitting round the contours of the canopy. Binoculars are particularly helpful in observing it. However, with the deaths of so many mature elms, the butterfly has re-established itself on sucker-growth in hedgerows, and is as a result much easier to observe. In some seasons, the butterflies can be seen in considerable numbers nectaring on creeping thistle (*Cirsium arvense*) or bramble (*Rubus spp.*) blossom. When at rest or nectaring, they always keep their wings closed, so only the distinctive under-side is visible. Frequent movement between trees up to 300 metres apart has been observed, and it seems that the butterfly readily disperses to colonise new sites.

Distribution and Status:

Historical-

Under the mis-nomer 'black hairstreak', Jermyn listed it as occurring in hedges and gardens at Ramsey and Wrabness. Other 19th century reports include Raynor who noted it was 'very abundant' in the Maldon district; and Fitch who listed it from Hazeliegh and North Fambridge, St Lawrence, Witham, Writtle, Bergholt woods, near Colchester, between Colchester and Halstead, Ramsey and Wrabness (the latter records coming from Harwood). Harwood himself regarded it as so widespread that it was unnecessary to mention any specific localities: it occurred wherever wych elm grew. Laidlaw stated it was 'locally plentiful' around Woodham Mortimer in 1946, between 1st and 25th July, whilst Friedlein writing of the area around North Fambridge, noted that in 1947 it 'was to be seen in thousands all over this part of Essex', but in 1950 was entirely absent. In the 1950s and early '60's Friedlein maintained a protected habitat for white-letter hairstreaks on his farm at North Fambridge. Here they flourished until at least the early 1960s, while colonies in local woods declined to near-extinction, along with other woodland species. Clark and Hobday, reporting on their 1963 survey, gave Colchester, West Bergholt, Coggeshall and Weeley as localities in the North East of the county. Firmin et al. noted the high incidence of Dutch Elm disease since 1971 as having destroyed notable sites. However, there were still strong colonies in the Colchester area, particularly at Friday and Donyland Woods and at West Bergholt. Benton observed a large colony on the northern fringe of the campus of the University of Essex from 1979 until its apparent demise by 1982, after the felling of the diseased elms upon which the larvae were feeding. Benton reported the re-discovery of small populations of the butterfly in the Roman River valley during 1984 by Jonathan Greenwood and Brian Goodey, after several fruitless searches in previous years. Intensive searches in the early 1980s revealed several previously unknown colonies, though in each numbers seemed small. Goodey and Firmin gave it as still widespread and frequent in North East Essex at the beginning of the 1990s.

Jermyn 1827, Raynor 1884, Fitch 1891, Harwood 1903, Laidlaw 1950, Friedlein 1951, note in Essex Naturalist1966, Clark & Hobday, 1966, Firmin et al. 1975, Benton 1984, Goodey & Firmin 1992).

Current-
The butterfly remains widespread in our area, and is probably under-recorded. It occurs on elm sucker-growth in Hill House Wood, West Bergholt, at various sites in the Roman River Valley, close to the Farmhouse on Old Hall Marsh (RSPB Reserve), in lanes between Alresford and Brightlingsea, at Mistley and in a garden at Langenhoe. Thistle or bramble flowers close to hedge-row and woodland elms where sucker-growth has commenced flowering should be observed in July for evidence of this butterfly.

SMALL COPPER (*Lycaena phlaeas*)   Plate 6

Description:
(Wing span from 32-35 mm.)This species could not be confused with any other likely to be seen in our district. The ground-colour of the upper-side fore-wings is a bright, shining copper-colour (fading somewhat with age), with a black outer border and a distinctive pattern of black spots. The hind-wings are black with a copper-coloured band towards the hind edge. There is often a more-or-less well defined row of blue spots along the inner edge of the orange band. Where this is well developed the insect has a particularly fine appearance. The under-side hind-wing is pale brownish, with faint black markings and a narrow reddish band towards the outer edge. The ground-colour of the under-side fore-wing is pale copper-coloured with a pattern of black spots resembling that on the upper-side. There is a variable slight 'tail' on the rear edge of the hind-wings. The females are very similar to the males but on average a little larger.

Similar Species:
The small copper belongs to a group of very beautiful butterflies represented by some eight other species in Europe. The only other species to occur in Britain is the large copper (*L. dispar*), but the indigenous population died out before 1850. There have been several re-introductions of populations from Europe, but these have not so far proved very successful. In any case, the fenland habitat for the large copper is not present in Essex, so we are unlikely ever to have a local population. The combination of a bright copper ground colour with black markings of the small copper is therefore quite distinctive.

Life History:
The white eggs are laid on the upper-surface of the leaves of the food-plant, usually close to the stem. The caterpillars are yellow at first but older ones are plain green or green with pink stripes. They feed on the under-side of the leaves of sorrel (*Rumex acetosa*) or sheep's sorrel (*R. acetosella*). The pupa is brown, and said to be found in leaf-litter. The butterfly often has three generations in a year in our area, with the first generation of adults flying through May and into June, the second in July and August, and the third in September and October. The winter is passed in the caterpillar stage.

26

Habitat and Behaviour:
The most favoured haunts of the small copper butterfly are dry, heathy slopes facing the sun, where the food-plants are abundant. They also inhabit rough, scrubby grassland, disused sand-and-gravel pits, ex-industrial sites, open places in woods, coastal 'cliffs' and sea-walls, and gardens where appropriately managed. They must have lost much habitat to building development and agricultural intensification, but also to past declines in rabbit-grazing.

The butterflies are usually met with in small numbers, widely dispersed over their habitats. They generally bask, wings open, on the ground or on low-growing vegetation, but can also be seen, sometimes congregating together, on flowers - especially thistles - in Summer and Autumn.

Distribution and Status:
Historical-
Although generally regarded as a common butterfly, its population has apparently fluctuated considerably. According to Fitch it was common and widespread throughout Essex, but less common than formerly. However, Cole, writing about East Mersea, reported a recovery of the small copper population in 1893, after a period when it had seemed to be disappearing. Harwood, writing a decade later, mentioned it as common, especially on the coast. Pratt noted its scarcity throughout the county in 1949, but Clark and Hobday, writing of their 1963 survey, regarded it as 'common and widespread' in North East Essex. Firmin et al. noted the causes of habitat loss, but saw it as widespread and still common where optimal habitat remained. A similar picture emerges from Emmet and Pyman and Goodey and Firmin, with 1991 given as a year of exceptional abundance.

(Fitch 1891, Cole (note in Essex Naturalist) 1893, Harwood 1903, Pratt 1951, Clark & Hobday 1966, Firmin et al. 1975, Emmet & Pyman 1985, Goodey & Firmin 1992)

Current-
As indicated in the historical record, numbers fluctuate considerably from year to year, but the species remains fairly common and widespread wherever there is suitable habitat. Corke (1997) considers the species in decline in Essex generally, and advocates research into its exact habitat requirements and host/parasite interactions. Consistently with Harwood's comment, it is well-established along the coasts and estuaries, at Copt Hall, Little Wigborough; Cudmore Grove Country Park, East Mersea; Goldhanger; the Naze at Walton; Holland Haven Country Park, and the 'cliffs' at Clacton and Frinton. Inland it is often very common at Markshall, and also occurs on Hilly Fields, Colchester, the University of Essex campus, the Roman River Valley and many other places.

BROWN ARGUS *(Aricia agestis)*   Plates 6, 7

Description:

Like the other 'blues', this species is small (average wing-span 29mm). The upper-sides of the wings are dark brown (paler in worn specimens) in both sexes, with a row of crescent-shaped orange markings towards the outer edge of both fore and hind-wings. There is a black spot at the centre of the fore-wings. The under-sides are pale grey-brown (usually darker in the females) with a row of orange markings round the edges, and black-centred 'eye' markings.

Similar species:

In our district, the only other butterfly likely to be confused with the brown argus is the female of the common blue. These generally have at least some blue scales on the upper-sides, especially towards the base of the wings, whereas the brown argus does not. However, some female common blues do have very little blue scaling, and so a closer look is needed. There are two definitive characteristics, both visible only on the under-side (see figs. 2a and 2b). On the under-side fore-wing of the common blue there is a spot on the fore-wing between the cell-spot and the base of the wing. Unfortunately, when the butterfly settles with its wings closed this 'sometimes' is out of sight. The second character is the row of black spots on the hind-wing under-side. These form a regular series in the common blue, but in the brown argus one of those on the leading edge of the wing is displaced towards the middle of the wing, giving a colon (:) appearance.

Fig. 2a: Common blue under-side   Fig. 2b: Brown argus under-side

Life History:

There are two generations each year. The white eggs are laid on the leaves of rock rose (*Helianthemum chamaecistus*) on chalk and limestone downland, but in our area the leaves of various geranium species (mainly *G. dissectum* and *G. molle*) are used. The caterpillars are green, with a pink line along the side. They feed on the leaves from below, leaving the upper cuticle of the leaves intact. They are reputedly always attended by ants, which feed on a sweet substance secreted by the caterpillars, and the chrysalis is buried by the ants in a cell. It is believed that the ants protect the caterpillars and chrysalids from parasitic insects. The adult butterflies can be seen in May and June (first brood), and their offspring (second brood) from late July through into September. The caterpillars resulting from eggs laid by the second generation females hibernate through the winter, and start feeding again the next spring.

Habitat and Behaviour:

The typical habitat for this species is chalk and limestone downland. However, in our part of Essex it is found on sea walls and adjacent grazing marshes, rough grassland, roadside verges, unmanaged open spaces and ex-industrial ('brown-field') sites in the towns, and woodland clearings. Asher et al. (2001) say that larval foodplants growing in short turf are preferred, though this may apply particularly to the downland colonies. In our area the butterfly often colonises areas with rank vegetation, though always with one or more geranium species present.

Status and Distribution:

The brown argus is subject to periodic fluctuations in its abundance and geographical range, as indicated from what we know of its history in North East Essex.

Historical -

During the 19th century it was regarded as a local species, though not rare, in Essex as a whole. Jermyn reported it from the parsonage lawn and cliffs, Wrabness, and according to Mathew it was 'rare at Parkeston'. Under the name '*Lycaena astrarche*', H. Vaughan reported seeing one specimen at Hadleigh castle in the south of Essex in 1860 and Raynor reported it as sometimes common but local at Hazeleigh. For the county as a whole, Fitch (1891) regarded it as 'not rare but local'. However, up until that time it seems that it was very scarce in our part of Essex, as Fitch reports Harwood as not having taken as many as twenty specimens. There was a sudden influx in 1896, however, when it 'abounded in all directions', and continued to hold its ground, though in smaller numbers, up to Harwood's report for the Victoria County History. It must have declined subsequently. There is only one literature reference to it - noted on an EFC outing to Maldon, on Aug. 16th 1952 - until 1975, when Firmin et al. described it as very local, having disappeared from many of its former haunts in the county. It formerly occurred in small numbers on the heath-lands of the Roman River Valley, during the years between the two World Wars it was present on Hilly Fields, Colchester, and there were colonies at Copford, West Bergholt and Fordham up to the 1960s. A few were seen on Hilly Fields in the early 1950s, presumably signs of the persistence of the pre-war colony. However, there were no records from North East Essex between the early 1970s and 1983. In that year two worn males were seen, quite independently, one by Greenwood in the Roman River Valley, and one by Benton near Dovercourt. These were presumed to be vagrants from surviving colonies in South Essex, over the border in Suffolk, or possibly even from the Continent. However, sightings on the Dengie peninsular, near Maldon and at Colne Point in 1986 raised hopes that a recovery of the species in our part of Essex was under way (Firmin 1986b).

(*Jermyn 1827, Mathew: Colchester Natural History Museum collection, Raynor 1884, Fitch 1891, Harwood 1903, Essex Naturalist vol.29, Firmin 1978a, Firmin 1986b, Benton 1983*).

Current-

The early 1990s saw a sudden increase in the range of this species especially in central and south eastern England. This was very marked in North East Essex, beginning with the discovery of a colony at East Mersea by Linda and Joe Firmin, and the butterfly's subsequent spread into many suitable habitats throughout our area. Firmin gives Markshall Estate, Coggeshall; Earls Colne; West Bergholt; Fordham; Great Horkesley; Wivenhoe; Brightlingsea and the whole of the Roman River Valley as localities during 1996 - 7. The butterfly was also present on open spaces, such as 'the Moors' in Colchester, and many other places. There appears to have been some retraction since the late 1990s, though it remains quite widespread in our area (e.g. Copt Hall, Little Wigborough and Hilly Fields, Colchester in spring 2002). Corke (1997) considers proposed explanations for the marked fluctuations in abundance and range of this species, including weather, parasite interactions, set-aside, variations in rabbit populations and possible shifts to new food-plants. He favours a combination of factors, particularly weather and parasites. Firmin's observation of a female laying on mallow (*Malva sylvestris*) is of interest in this regard. Further study of this butterfly in the field - its food-plants, ant associations and parasites will be of great interest. (*Asher et al. 2001, Firmin 1995a, Bailey 1994, Firmin 1999a, Corke 1997*)

COMMON BLUE   (*Polyommatus icarus*)   Plate 7

Description:

A very familiar butterfly, this species is quite small (average wing-span 35mm.). The male has a bright blue upper-side, unmarked except for a very fine black marginal line around the wing-edges. Usually, there are inconspicuous black markings extending slightly into the white wing-fringes, especially at the ends of the veins. The female upper-sides are quite variable. They have a row of orange crescent-shaped spots around the edge of both fore and hind wings. Along the outer-edge of these is a row of black spots, generally more clearly marked on the hind-wings. Usually, the orange crescents fade to whitish towards the apex of the fore-wings. The ground colour of the upper-sides is generally dark brown, but with varying amounts of purple-blue scaling. Sometimes this is reduced to an area close to the body, but it can sometimes extend over most of the wing-surface out to the orange crescents. The under-sides in both sexes have a characteristic pattern of small black-centred 'eye' markings, with a row of orange crescents (similar to the upper-side female pattern) round the edges. The ground-colour is grey in the males, and greyish brown in the females, with a variable 'flush' of bluish and golden scales at the wing-bases.

Similar Species:
The common blue could be confused with the Adonis blue (*P. bellargus*), but this is a species of chalk and limestone downland which does not occur in, or even close to our area. The holly blue (*C. argiolus*) is our only other 'blue blue', and it differs from the common blue in having a plain pale blue under-side with small black spots, and no orange markings. The most likely confusion is between brown forms of the female common blue and either sex of the brown argus. See under the latter species for distinguishing features.

Life History:
There are usually two generations each year. The first brood fly from the latter part of May and through June, the second in August and September. In favourable years there may be a third generation. The pale white eggs are laid singly on the young shoots of the larval food-plant. This is commonly one of the bird's-foot trefoils (*Lotus corniculatus, uliginosus* or *glaber*), but they can sometimes be found on restharrows (*Ononis spp.*) and black medick (*Medicago lupulina*). The slug-shaped caterpillar is plain green, and it feeds by day on the leaves of its food-plant. It is attended by ants for which it secretes a sugary solution. The green chrysalis is generally buried by the ants. The winter is passed in the caterpillar stage.

Habitat and Behaviour:
The typical habitats of this species in our area are sheltered patches of unimproved grassland, post-industrial 'brown-field' sites, grass verges, cuttings and banks, sea walls, grazing marshes and agricultural 'set-aside'. The larval food-plants often flourish on recently cleared or disturbed soil, and the butterflies are often quick to colonise such newly-created habitats. The males can often be seen near the tops of grass stems early in the morning, after cloudy spells, or towards the end of sunny days with wings spread wide-open facing the setting sun. Like many other 'blue' species, they roost head-down, high on the stems of grasses or other tall herbs. The males 'patrol' actively in search of females, stopping occasionally to take nectar from flowers of bird's-foot trefoil, clovers or other plants. Females are less active, spending much of their time nectaring or ovipositing on suitable food-plants.

Distribution and Status:
Historical-
According to W.H. Harwood (1903) it was 'abundant everywhere, especially on the coast'. All the early writers make similar assessments.
Current-
Along with many other species, the common blue has undoubtedly been badly affected by the combination of building development and the industrialised farming of our district. However, it remains widespread in North East Essex, and although it is now confined to limited areas of suitable habitat, it remains quite common, and sometimes abundant in these. It is often to be found on the sea walls and grassy areas adjacent to

them, such as at Goldhanger, Frinton, East Mersea, Tollesbury and Old Hall. Inland it occurs at Hillhouse Wood (West Bergholt), Gosbecks Archaeological Park, High Woods Country Park, and Hilly Fields (Colchester), the Roman River Valley and in many other places.

HOLLY BLUE   (*Celastrina argiolus*)   Plate 7, 8

Description:
Similar to other blues in size, the holly blue has an average wing-span of 35mm. The males have bright, sky-blue upper-sides, appearing lighter along the veins. A fine black line, dividing the wing edges from the white fringes, thickens slightly to invade the lamina of the wing towards the apex of the fore-wings. The female upper-side also has a blue ground-colour, but with wide black margins, shading into the blue basal areas, to both fore and hind-wings. There is a narrow black 'discal' mark in the middle of each fore-wing. In both males and females the under-sides of the wings are pale silvery-blue with black markings.

Similar Species:
In North East Essex the only similar species is the common blue. In flight males of the two species can look very similar, though their flight patterns and habitats are different. If close examination is possible, then the lack of orange markings on the holly blue under-side is definitive. The slight black suffusion towards the apex of the male fore-wings, and the wide black borders, un-marked by orange crescents, in the females, also separates the holly from the common blue.

Life-History:
There are two generations each year and, uniquely, the caterpillars of the first and second generation feed on different plants. The first generation of adults flies between late March and late June. The females lay their white, disc-shaped eggs on the flowers or flower-buds of the food-plant. This is usually holly (*Ilex aquifolium*) in the Spring. The caterpillars emerge within about two weeks, and feed on the flowers or fruits as they develop. The caterpillars are slug-shaped and pale green in colour, often with reddish markings on the sides and a pale line along the back when fully grown. They leave the food-plant to pupate. The pupae hatch from late July onwards, to form the second generation of adults. These fly through August and on into September, usually laying their eggs on the flowers or flower-buds of ivy (*Hedera helix*). The resulting caterpillars continue feeding on the flowers and fruits, and go on to over-winter as chrysalids. In some years there is a third generation in October, and other shrubs, including spindle (*Euonymus europaeus*), bramble (*Rubus fruticosus*), gorse (*Ulex europaeus*) and snowberry (*Symphoricarpos rivularis*) have been recorded as larval food-plants. A female was observed laying an egg on a flower bud of pyracantha in a town-centre garden on 11/04/02 (*Benton*)

As is often the case in this family, the caterpillars secrete sugary substances which are attractive to ants. They are also heavily parasitised by a small wasp, *Listrodomus nycthemerus*. The parasites lay their eggs in the caterpillars, but these eggs to not develop until the caterpillar pupates. The parasite's larva then consumes the contents of the butterfly chrysalis, and emerges from the empty case as an adult, ready to repeat the cycle. Holly blue populations have huge cyclical fluctuations, with periods of great abundance followed by scarcity. It is believed that the mortality inflicted by the parasite is one of the main causes of this. (*Firmin 1990b, Revels 1994, Corke, 1997*)

Habitat and Behaviour:
This butterfly can often be found wherever the main food-plants grow, hedges with holly and ivy, woods and woodland-edges, scrubby 'waste' places and the like. However, it is most often seen in urban and suburban parks and gardens, where it often attracts the attention of observant non-entomologists, especially in periods of abundance. Both males and females tend to congregate around ivy or holly, depending on the time of year. The males are most evident, being both more active and more brightly coloured. They hold temporary territories, flying back, forth, and around the holly bushes or ivy-patches, contouring their outlines with great persistence. 'Courtship' involves a brief but rapid fluttering of the males' wings, presumably shedding pheromones. Both males and females bask with wings open early in the morning and after cool, cloudy spells. The females tend to stay close to the larval food-plant, but they settle more often and for longer than the males. In dull weather they settle in the vegetation with wings closed.

Status and Distribution:
Historical-
Fitch (1891) described it, under the name 'azure blue', as fairly common and generally distributed throughout the county. Harwood's (1903) assessment was similar, but he remarked that it was sometimes scarce in some districts. In 1900 and 1901 it had appeared in far greater numbers than ever before.
Current-
The holly blue has expanded its UK range in recent years, possibly as a result of climate change. In North East Essex it is common and widespread, though still subject to fluctuations in its population. It is particularly common in gardens in the Lexden Road area of Colchester, in the vicinity of Wivenhoe Wood, around holly trees on the campus of Essex University and in many other places throughout our area.

WHITE ADMIRAL   (*Ladoga camilla*)   Plate 8

Description:
A fairly large butterfly (wing-span 64mm.), the upper-side is brownish-black, marked with white, whilst the under-side is beautifully patterned in orange-red, white, black

33

and blue-grey. Occasionally there are aberrational forms of the white admiral when the white fore-wing bands are obscured, giving an almost black, sooty appearance. This form, *obliterae*, was captured by Ian Rose in Weeleyhall Wood in the late 1940s and another was captured by John Pearce in Donyland Wood in July, 1955 and was illustrated in Nature in North East Essex 1956.

Life History:
The female lays eggs in late June or July on leaves of honeysuckle (*Lonicera periclymenum*) that grow along edges of woodland rides and glades or overhang a ditch. A single egg is deposited towards the edge of a leaf's upper surface. The surface of the olive-green egg has a honeycomb pattern and is covered with spines. Hatching is in about a week. The newly-hatched larva (2mm long) is greenish-ochre in colour with a granular appearance and a black head. Towards the end of August, after the second moult, it prepares for hibernation by securing a leaf to a stem with silk and drawing the basal edges of the leaf together to form a little tent (hibernaculum) in which it hibernates until the following March or April. The full-grown larva is green on the back and sides, marked with yellow and purplish beneath the white lateral stripe. The head is brown and there are reddish-brown spines along the back. The pupa is suspended by tail hooks from a pad of silk attached to a honeysuckle stem or leaf. It is green marked with purple-brown and adorned with metallic silvery spots. The butterfly hatches in two weeks.

Habitat and Behaviour:
The white admiral is the most elegant of British woodland butterflies, gliding in and out of dappled shade and spending much of its life in the canopy where it basks on oak (*Quercus spp.*) leaves and drinks aphid honeydew. Often the butterflies are to be seen gliding among the trees, or descending to feed at bramble blossom. According to Harwood, writing in 1884 'it is only found when the 'slop', or underwood is high, and a considerable clearance in a small wood means sometimes the all but total extermination of the species in that particular wood, but colonists from neighbouring woods soon restore the balance, so soon as favourable conditions again obtain, but when there is no neighbouring wood, the balance may never be restored'. Fragmentation of woodland habitats and changing woodland management have undoubtedly affected the fortunes of this butterfly, but in addition it is liable to considerable fluctuations in population from year to year, and also to expansions and contractions of range. Research done in the 1970s concluded that predation by birds on the caterpillars was a major factor affecting white admiral populations. Good weather during the later stages of the caterpillars' development enabled them to complete their life-cycle quickly, thus reducing the toll of predation. However, it now seems that a number of other factors, including feeding on the food-plant by muntjac deer, also affect survival rates.
(*Harwood, 1884, Hall 1981, Corke 1997, Pollard 1979, Pollard & Cooke 1994*).

Status and Distribution:

Historical-

One was brought to John Ray from near Tollesbury on July 11 1695. Jermyn gave Hartley Wood, St Osyth as a locality in the early 19th century, and Edward Doubleday reported it as common at Great Bromley in 1836. Harwood, writing in 1903, stated that the white admiral was found in most of the larger woods in north Essex and, in the closing years of the 19th century, was abundant in some of them. However, this seems not to have been true of the rest of Essex, as Fitch, writing in 1891 regarded it as rare and declining. The butterfly retreated from most of its former Essex haunts until a general expansion of its range again took place between 1930 and the early 1940s, possibly due to a combination of favourable weather and the decline of commercial coppice management of woods. However, another decline set in during the 1950s, and it was thought to have become extinct in North East Essex by the mid 1960s. However, white admirals were still to be seen in good numbers in Friday Wood in the summer of 1959. In Joe Firmin's notebook for June 29, 1959 is the entry:"*L. camilla* quite plentiful in Donyland and Friday Wood. At least six seen in central ride of Friday Wood. On previous day I visited Hartley Wood, Little Clacton where I saw two white admirals and also one high brown fritillary". It now seems likely that the butterfly persisted in small numbers at one of its long-standing strong-holds, Stour Wood, Wrabness.

Current-

The white admiral, as far as is known at present, is now confined to two woodland sites, both in North Essex. The main surviving site is Stour Wood, Wrabness where a small but viable colony has existed for many years. The second site is at Friday Wood, Berechurch where Dr Chris Gibson of English Nature, while on a survey of invertebrates, saw two white admirals on July 14, 1995. This was a well known habitat for the species until its dramatic decline in the late 1960s in most of its then-known Essex sites. Subsequent visits by CNHS members show that there is now a small colony with 10 or more being seen in June and July. It is not clear whether these butterflies are the result of recolonisation or whether they have been introduced without notification. It seems unlikely that survivors from the 1950s and 1960s could have remained undetected in what is one of the most regularly surveyed habitats near Colchester. Hopes remain that the white admiral may naturally recolonise some of its former strongholds as has happened nearby in east Suffolk. Reg Arthur found specimens in Riddles Wood, St Osyth in the 1980s but none has been located since.

SMALL TORTOISESHELL (*Aglais urticae*)   Plate 9

Description:

Another normally common and much-loved species. The upper-side ground colour is reddish-orange with patches of black, white and yellow. The margins of both fore and hind-wings have a series of blue lunules. The under-side is mainly blackish-brown

marked with paler areas. Wingspan: male 50mm; female 56mm.
Sometimes striking aberrational forms of the butterfly occur and these include *semi-ichnusoides* where there are large dark patches on fore-wings and hind-wings, believed to be caused by high temperature in the pupal stage. In the aberration *lutea* the ground colour is yellow or buff.

Life History:

After winter hibernation, pairing takes place in the spring. Eggs are laid in batches on the under-side of young nettle (*Urtica dioica*) leaves. Each clear green egg has nine longitudinal keels. The eggs hatch in 10 days. After the first moult the ground colour of the larva is yellow and the colour becomes steadily darker. After the final moult larvae, which live gregariously in webs until the final instar, are either yellowish densely speckled with black and marked with yellow lines and spines, or black with yellowish spines. The larval stage lasts about a month. At the end, larvae leave the web and live singly or in small groups sometimes spinning edges of nettle leaves together to form a shelter similar to that formed by red admiral larvae. The pupa is suspended by tail hooks from a pad of silk attached to a nearby plant stem. Its colour varies from dark brown to pinkish-brown with patches of gold colouring. The butterfly hatches in two weeks. The small tortoiseshell is found in a wide range of habitats and is a frequent visitor to gardens where it feeds on flowers including buddleia, sedum, michaelmas daisy, dahlia and African marigold. It hibernates as a butterfly from October onwards, usually in sheds or outhouses. Sometimes the hibernators appear early during mild days in February, but most emerge in March and April to feed on garden spring flowers and on sallow (*Salix spp.*) bloom along edges of woods and hedges.

Status and Distribution:

Although considered to be one of our commonest and more widely distributed butterflies the small tortoiseshell does have periods of low density and experienced a relatively scarce phase from 1999 until 2002, being almost absent from some districts in North Essex. These cyclical variations in population are well documented and may be caused by a variety of factors including climatic effects on the larval stage and increased bird predation and parasitism.

PEACOCK (*Inachis io*) Plate 9

Description:

One of the most popular, common and unmistakable of British butterflies. The upper-side ground colour is brownish-red with distinctive blue and black eye markings. The under-side of the wings is black, crossed by fine black lines and with a whitish dot in the centre of the hind-wings. Wingspan: 63mm.

Life History:
After winter hibernation and spring pairing the female lays batches of olive green eggs on the under-side of young leaves of stinging nettle (*Urtica dioica*). They hatch in two weeks. After the first moult the larva's ground colour is olive brown and the colour darkens. When the larva is fully grown after the fourth moult it is velvety black with white dots and black spines. The larvae live gregariously moving from one nettle plant to another in groups. Occupied and deserted webs are very conspicuous. The larval stage lasts a month. The pupa is suspended by tail hooks from a pad of silk attached to any suitable support. The butterfly hatches in two weeks.

Habitat and Behaviour:
The peacock feeds on the nectar of flowers wherever they are found in woods, marshes and gardens. The butterfly hibernates from October until March usually in sheds, hollow trees, wood piles and houses. Sometimes several hibernate in tree holes and when disturbed produce an audible rustling sound by opening and closing their wings, presumably to deter a would-be predator. They are a familiar sight as they sun-bathe in sheltered sun-spots early in the spring after hibernation. The summer brood spend much of their time building up their reserves for winter hibernation by taking nectar - often from garden flowers. Hemp agrimony, thistles, buddleia, dahlias, michaelmas daisies and African marigolds are favourites. Males are strongly territorial, and will chase off intruding males from their chosen 'sun-spots'.

Status and Distribution:
A very abundant butterfly in the past. In 1900 'the nettles about Colchester were black with the larvae in the early part of July, and in August the perfect insects visited the clover fields in enormous numbers' (*Harwood, 1903*). The butterfly does not now occur in such numbers, but it remains a very familiar sight in open spaces, parks, gardens and woodland rides throughout our area.

COMMA   (*Polygonia c-album*)   Plate 9
Description:
The jagged outline of the wings is unique among British butterflies. The upper-side is a rich orange-brown marked with black and yellowish brown. The under-side in the typical form is dark, with shades of brown and bronze-green. In the centre of the hind-wing under-side is a white comma-shaped mark from which the species gets its name. Females are larger than the males and have slightly less jagged wing edges. A proportion of the butterflies which appear in June and July belong to the seasonal form known as *hutchinsoni*. In these the ground colour is paler on the upper-side, and the under-side is much paler.
Occasionally there are aberrational forms such as *suffusa* where there are black or dark brown patches on all wings or aberration *sagitta* where the hind-wings are suffused with dark brown. An example of this form was captured by Joe Firmin at Friday

Wood, Berechurch, on August 8th 1958.

Life History:

Hibernated butterflies fly in March and after pairing females lay eggs singly or in small batches on the upper edges of stinging nettle (*Urtica dioica*)leaves or on hop (*Humulus lupulus*) leaves. Other foodplants are elm (*Ulmus spp.*), sallow (*Salix spp.*) and currant (*Ribes*). The green egg has 11 longitudinal keels which give it a glassy appearance. Hatching takes place after 1/2 weeks. The full-grown larva is tan coloured with a gleaming splash of white on the rear half of the back and with yellowish spines. It resembles a bird dropping. The larval stage lasts from six to seven weeks. The pupa is formed low down on vegetation and camouflaged to resemble a withered leaf. It hatches after 1/2 weeks. The resulting butterflies are on the wing from July to mid September. Those of the dark form continue feeding, but do not engage in reproductive activity. They eventually go into hibernation and continue the reproductive cycle the following spring. Meanwhile, the pale specimens (*hutchinsoni*) start to breed soon after they emerge from the chrysalis, and their offspring reach maturity in late summer, when they also go on to hibernate. Before hibernation they can be seen feeding on garden flowers, ivy bloom, also on the juices of ripe blackberries and fallen apples and pears. They enter hibernation in the autumn on tree trunks or where dead leaves accumulate. The jagged wing edges and brown under-side provide a remarkable camouflage resembling a dead leaf.

Habitat and Behaviour:

Commas, although visitors to gardens, favour clearings and open rides in woods. Males establish territories in sunny nooks in spring, taking up positions on branches and leaves, leaning forward with wings half open. They intercept any butterfly or insect passer-by in swift, high-speed flight during which their wings flash bright orange brown. After a thorough investigation they return to their perches or if the intruder is a female, give chase. Pairing takes place high on a tree or shrub. The female then wanders off to seek suitable plants for egg laying. In early spring, after hibernation, they can be seen basking, wings fully spread, on patches of bare ground in full sunshine.

Status and Distribution:

Historical-

The disappearance of the comma from eastern and Southern England from the end of the 19th century until the 1930s and its recolonisation of its lost territory is an interesting example of natural recovery. In the 19th century there was a decline in hop gardens which robbed the species of a popular larval foodplant and the new techniques of vine burning and washing with insecticides must have exacerbated the situation. Fitch, writing in 1890, declared it 'very rare if not now extinct in the county, like the hop industry', while a decade later Harwood reported that W. Tillaney had captured several near Colchester in 1850, but 'only stragglers' had been seen since. Whatever the reasons, the comma retreated to the west country and the Welsh borders and females

adapted to egg laying on nettles and elm leaves before the spread of Dutch elm disease. The comeback of the comma to Essex and the eastern counties began in the late 1930s (first reports in Essex Naturalist for 1934, and affirmed as 'well established' again in the county by 1940). By the mid 1940s it had become widespread once more, even common in some areas.
(*Fitch 1991, Harwood 1903, Firmin et al. 1975*)

Current-
The comma is now widespread and common in woods, hedgerows and gardens throughout North East Essex, and is currently more often seen than the small tortoiseshell.

SILVER-WASHED FRITILLARY (*Argynnis paphia*)   Plate 10

Description:
This large butterfly (wing span 54-70mm) is of a distinctive orange-brown colour in the males with the females a darker, more olive shade. The males have four thick black ridges along the veins of the fore-wings which are scent glands known as androconial organs. The silver-washed gets its popular name from the delicate greens and silver streaks, rather like a water-colour wash, on the hind-wings of both sexes. The females are usually larger, and often have a deep green tint to the orange-brown upper-sides upper-sides. Extreme forms of this are known as *valezina*, and have been known from North East Essex (*Firmin et al. 1975*).

Similar Species:
The only other (smaller) butterfly with the vivid colouration of the male silver- washed is the comma, otherwise there can be no real confusion with other species.

Life History:
The female silver-washed lays her eggs in the chinks of bark of oak (*Quercus spp.*) trees, usually 1 to 2 metres above ground level. Sometimes eggs are laid on dead bracken (*Pteridium aquilinum*). The egg is cone shaped and pale yellowish-white. The egg hatches about two weeks after being laid in July or early August, but the tiny caterpillar does no more than eat the eggshell before spinning a tiny pad of silk on which it hibernates, still on the tree trunk. It descends to ground level the following spring and immediately starts looking for violets (*Viola spp.*) on which to feed. The caterpillar's feeding bites are easy to detect as they are curved in the sides of the leaves. The caterpillar itself is much harder to spot as it spends most of its day basking in shafts of sunlight, often on dead leaves up to 30cm from the violet clump. The spiky, full-grown, caterpillar is purple-brown, streaked buff and black. The chrysalis, suspended beneath a leaf or twig, looks very like a curled-up dead leaf with silvery patches. The butterfly emerges from late June and up to the first week of August.

Habitat and Behaviour:
Essentially a species of woodland with open glades and rides but it also flies in lanes bordering woods. Adults of both sexes spend long periods on tree tops drinking aphid honeydew but they also descend to feed on the nectar of bramble blossom and thistles. Silver-washed fritillaries engage in beautiful aerobatic courtship flights. The males fly in zig-zag fashion 1 to 2m above ground level seeking females. The females fly in a straight line while the males repeatedly swoop under them, then up in front of their heads. Since the females do not lay their eggs on the caterpillars' food-plant, but some distance away, in crevices in the bark of oak trees, it is essential that the tiny caterpillars can reach the violets the following spring. At 12.00 noon on 27/07/02 the authors observed a female at Markshall fluttering and walking on low-growing vegetation around the base of several oak trees. This behaviour is believed to ensure that there is sufficient food plant in the vicinity of the tree. The specimen we watched occasionally flew up to the lower branches of the nearest tree and then down again, presumably to ensure that she was close to the tree-trunk. It subsequently flew up to the tree-trunk, about one metre above the ground, wings partly open, and squeezed its body into a crack in the bark, presumably egg-laying. It then made its way up the trunk, stopping four more times to repeat the process, the final stop being some five metres above ground level.

Status and Distribution:
According to Jermyn the silver-washed fritillary occurred in Lexden and Stour woods, Bromley Thickets and Hamlet Wood, as well as at Beaumont in the early decades of the 19th century. Later in the century it was said to be common at Donyland and St. Osyth, but had become scarce at High Woods, Colchester. The species seems to have vanished from most of the rest of Essex in the early decades of the 20th century, but became quite common and widespread again during the 1930s. It may have been continuously present in the woods of North East Essex through this period, and was certainly widespread and often common in several of them, especially Donyland Wood, Friday Wood and Weeleyhall Wood, until another decline took place in the 1950s, leading to its apparent extinction in our area at the end of the 1950s. They were also found into the 1960s in the woods of the Markshall Estate, Coggeshall and it is in some of these that efforts are being made under the Essex Biodiversity Action Plan to reintroduce silver-washed fritillaries and other woodland butterfly species which disappeared in the post-war period. The first female fritillaries were released in July, 1999, and early indications of success came in July, 2000, when offspring from the introduced females, which came from a donor site in Surrey, were seen in and near the original Markshall release site. Up to 10 were seen in any one day during July and August 2000. A further 8 females and 3 males were introduced in August, 2000. In July 2001 a further 12 females were released and an encouraging number of both males and females descendants from the two liberations, were seen in July and August 2001. There will be reinforcement from selected donor sites in the next three years to ensure success. An encouraging sign was that the egg-laying behaviour noted above took place some

distance from the initial release site. (*Jermyn 1827, Fitch 1891, Harwood 1903, Firmin 1962, Firmin et al. 1975, Firmin 2001a*).

SPECKLED WOOD   (*Pararge aegeria*)   Plate 10

Description:

The upper-side is dark brown with straw-yellow spots, some of which contain 'eye' markings. The under-side of the fore-wings is similar but the under-side hind-wings are lighter brown with darker, sometimes purplish, brown markings. The males are smaller and darker than the females and with more pointed wings. They have patches of scent scales on the fore-wings. Wingspan: male 47mm; female 50mm.

Life History:

First brood females appear in late March and in April. They lay yellowish-white eggs singly on grass blades and the larvae hatch after 10 days. The larva is green with darker green lines after its first moult. Pupation is after a month. The pupa is attached to a pad of silk on a grass stem or on a nearby plant. Its colour is variable and may be any shade of green or greenish-brown. The butterfly (second brood) hatches after three weeks. This brood flies in late June, to August or early September. There is usually a final emergence of adults in autumn. These are offspring of the second brood with which they also overlap. This third brood is usually not very numerous as by late summer most caterpillars develop slowly and overwinter or form hibernating pupae. The hibernating pupae produce the first adults of spring but these overlap with others which spend winter as larvae. This results in two peaks of emergence, the first in mid-May and the second in early June.

Habitat and Behaviour:

The speckled wood is a lover of dappled shade in woods and in lanes but it also adapts to open country and, in recent years in North Essex, has even been found in gardens, allotments and parks during a big expansion of range and diversity of habitat. Males occupy sunny spots where a gap in the wood canopy allows the sun to cast a pool of light on the woodland floor. Small patches are occupied by a single male and he fiercely defends his territory against intruders. Trespassing males are attacked in aerial skirmishes. Both insects spiral round each other, bumping and clashing their wings as they rise to the canopy. After a short while the intruder is driven off and the male resumes his vigil on a leaf or bracken frond with wings expanded to get the warmth of the sun. Virgin females are also attracted to the patches of sunlight. A courtship dance follows and the female leads the excited male to the tree tops where mating occurs. Both sexes feed on aphid honeydew on tree leaves.

Status and Distribution:
Historical-
William Harwood wrote that the speckled wood was common in the eastern counties in the middle of the 19th century but by the close of the century had vanished completely from nearly all its former haunts. Harwood added that why this once widespread species had disappeared was a mystery for it was common in nearly every copse and shady place and abounded in some woods where it was quite unmolested by collectors. Apart from scattered reports of odd individuals, perhaps resulting from clandestine releases, the speckled wood seems to have remained extinct as an Essex breeding species until 1955 when there was recolonisation of sites in South Essex. The spread of the speckled wood in Essex since the 1950s has been one of the great success stories of the post-war period. It is now thought that some of these butterflies may have crossed the Thames from the Kent side where they had remained common in some localities. From the late 1950s there was a steady northward and westward spread and it had reached the Dengie Peninsula by the mid-1960s. (*Fitch 1891, Harwood 1903, Firmin 1966, Firmin et al. 1975, Firmin 1986a, Corke 1997*).
Current-
By the mid-1990s speckled woods were being reported from most wooded places in North Essex as well as in gardens, lanes and parks. Specimens were even being seen well inside Colchester, and the species remains widespread throughout our area. Milder winters may well have benefited the species as well as changes in woodland management.

WALL (*Lasiommata megera*)   Plate 11

Description:
The ground colour is orange-brown marked with blackish-brown and with white-pupilled eye spots. The under-side fore-wing is similar but paler, and the hind-wing greyish, marked with dark lines and eye spots. Males have a conspicuous band of scent scales on upper surface of the fore-wing. Wingspan: male 44mm; female 46mm.

Life History:
This butterfly has two generations, the first in May and early June; the second in August and September. Eggs, when newly laid, are green, and are laid singly on grass blades. After a few days egg colour changes to white or creamy white. The larva hatches in 10 days. On emergence it is buffish-yellow with a brown head, its body covered with fine hairs. After the first moult the ground colour is green. When full-grown the larva is bluish-green with white stripes. The pupa colour varies from bright green to almost black. It is suspended from a silk pad attached to a stem of the foodplant or other nearby plant. The butterfly hatches after two weeks. The larvae of the second brood overwinter.

Habitat and Behaviour:
The wall is a sun-loving species of dry, grassy places, edges of arable fields, warm pathways, and stony banks. As its name suggests it loves to bask on walls and the dry, bare earth patches along the edges of fields or on the dry paths at the top of sea walls. The butterflies bask with their wings held two thirds open, angled towards the sun. In this way they can raise their body temperature. Often a male wall is disturbed by walkers along paths or sea walls. The butterflies quickly settle again a few metres ahead. Perching males are sunning themselves while waiting for a virgin female to fly down the track.

Status and Distribution:
The wall has suffered periods of serious decline in North Essex. Until 1974 it was considered to be generally distributed and common but after the summer drought of 1976 there was a marked decline. Then, following a partial recovery, there was another loss of numbers in the decade before the end of the century. Pockets survived along the North Essex coast including East Mersea and Goldhanger. The latter site has sea walls and warm paths next to farm fields as well as plentiful nectar sources such as knapweed (*Centaurea nigra*) and thistle flowers. There were signs of slow recovery in years 2000 and 2001 coinciding with a marked increase in some coastal areas of East Suffolk. These fluctuations in the status of the wall in North East Essex mirror wider changes in central and southern England, where there have been marked declines inland, but relatively stable coastal populations. The butterfly needs quite high temperatures to fly (hence its habit of basking on bare surfaces) and is associated with dry, unfertilised grasslands. Climatic factors are believed to be the main influence on its populations, but other causes such as the level of rabbit grazing and agricultural intensification must also have important effects. It is also possible that the practice of set-aside fields in arable farming areas may help recovery in some areas. (*Fitch 1891, Firmin 1988a, Firmin 1990a, Corke 1997, Asher et al. 2001*)

MARBLED WHITE (*Melanargia galathea*)   Plate 11

Description:
The ground colour varies from white to cream, with black markings. The upper-side hind-wings bear blue-centred eyespots near the margin. The markings on the under-side are similar but paler, with bolder eyespots. Females are larger and paler than the males with browner markings on the under-side hind-wings.

Life history:
The butterfly flies from late June until early August. Females scatter their whitish, rounded eggs among grasses, often while in flight. The eggs hatch in about three weeks. The newly-hatched larva is pale straw coloured with reddish brown stripes. After a meal of its eggshell and a few nibbles of grass leaves, the larva hibernates until

early spring when it feeds on grass leaves. Main grass species eaten are sheep's fescue (*Festuca ovina*), cock's foot (*Dactylis glomerata*), and Timothy (*Phleum pratense*). When ready to pupate in June or July the larva lies on the surface of the ground beneath the grass without any attachment or cover. The pupa is brownish white with brown markings. The butterfly hatches in about three weeks.

Habitat and Behaviour:
The marbled white which, despite its white, black-chequered appearance is not a true 'white' but, in fact, one of the 'browns' (Satyrinae), is a butterfly of grassy places along sea walls, on downs, in woodland glades and along wide, grassy verges. It has a slow, fluttery flight and is fond of feeding on the flowers of thistles, knapweed and scabious. In Essex its main surviving strongholds have been along Thames-side and on Canvey Island where sometimes large numbers fly along the sea walls.

Status and Distribution:
According to Jermyn, writing in the 1820s, it occurred in 'moist woods', on Mersea Island, Stour and Hartley Wood. However, the butterfly seems to have become extinct as a breeding species in North East Essex by the end of the 19th century. Harwood mentioned occasional subsequent reports from the North East, but it was unclear whether these were 'occasional stragglers' from the marbled white's stronghold in South Essex, or evidence of an undiscovered colony. Much earlier it was found in grassy clearings in woods in the Coggeshall and Halstead areas until the end of the 18th century.

There was an attempt to reintroduce the marbled white into restored grassland in a disused landfill site, Martin's Meadow, St Osyth, in the 1980s but this failed after only one season. It is possible, however, that the species will naturally colonise north Essex from the south where it expanding its range. Some have reached the Dengie Peninsula and single specimens have been seen at West Mersea, Maldon and Layer Breton Heath. In July, 1997, Linda and Joe Firmin saw a male and female along the sea wall at Goldhanger, north of the Blackwater, which raised hopes of a spread into north Essex but none has been seen in subsequent seasons. There is high alert, however, at Essex Wildlife Trust's Tollesbury Wick reserve, which has an extensive run of grassy sea walls, and also at the RSPB's reserve at Old Hall Marshes, Tollesbury, for sightings of marbled whites and possible colonisation.

(*Jermyn 1827, Harwood 1903, Firmin et al. 1975, Corke 1997, Firmin & Goodey 2001*).

GATEKEEPER (*Pyronia tithonus*)   Plate 11

Description:
The ground colour is brownish-orange with dark brown markings. Near the apex of the fore-wing is a black spot which usually contains two white dots and there is a white-

pupilled spot near the anal angle of the hind-wing. The under-side of the hind-wing is marked with shades of brown and with white-centred spots. Males are smaller and brighter than the females with a conspicuous dark band of scent scales (androconia) in the centre of the fore-wing. Wingspan: male 40mm; female 47mm.

Life History:

When egg-laying the female crawls down to the base of grasses and lays a single egg which is usually attached to a grass blade or stem but sometimes is just dropped. When first laid the egg is pale yellow but later it becomes blotched with red-brown. It hatches after about three weeks. The newly-emerged larva is cream-coloured with red-brown stripes; later it is green or greenish-brown. It feeds only at night, resting low in the grass by day. It is rather slug-like in appearance and movement. It goes into hibernation in October and resumes feeding in March. The pupa is ochre-coloured streaked and spotted brown. It is suspended from a grass stem and the butterfly emerges after about three weeks.

Habitat and Behaviour:

The butterfly flies in July and August in grassy places, woodland rides and along hedgerows, hence its alternative vernacular name of 'hedge brown'. It is also common in suburban gardens and open spaces in towns. The adult butterflies feed on honey-dew secreted by ants, as well as on hedgerow flowers - most notably on bramble.

Status and Distribution:

This is a widespread and abundant species and seems to be increasing its range. It is particularly common along edges of woods and on hedge banks which are sunny and where medium and fine-leaved grasses grow. It is common in lightly managed urban open spaces, such as High Woods Country Park and Hilly Fields, Colchester. There are also big colonies along some North Essex sea walls at East Mersea, Copt Hall, Little Wigborough, and Goldhanger.

MEADOW BROWN (*Maniola jurtina*) Plate 12

Description:

The sexes of this common butterfly are very different. The upper-side of the male is dark brown. The fore-wing has a black band of scent scales and a white-pupilled black eye spot near the apex, often with a small orange spot below it. The under-side fore-wing is orange with a grey-brown border which matches the general colour of the hind-wing. The female is larger and the upper-side has much larger orange-brown patches and also lacks the scent scales. In both sexes the under-side hind-wing has a paler band across it and there are variable small spots towards the outer margin. The meadow brown is a variable species and in large colonies there are often individuals with white or creamy patches on some, or all wings.

45

Life history:
The meadow brown flies in numbers from late June until September. Eggs are laid singly, usually on dead grass blades. They are yellowish-white when first laid but after a week become covered with reddish blotches. They hatch in about three weeks. When newly emerged, the larva is buff-brown with red-brown lines but turns green when feeding commences. The final colour is green with darker green and white lines. There is partial hibernation low down among the grass, the larva emerging to feed during mild days in winter. Feeding is mainly at night. The larval stage lasts eight to nine months. The pupa is green with black stripes on the wing cases. It is suspended from a pad of silk attached to a grass stem. The butterfly emerges after three or four weeks.

Habitat and Behaviour:
The butterflies occur, sometimes in great abundance, on rough grassland, coastal grazing marshes and hay meadows. The larvae feed on several different grass species and the females seek fine or medium-leaved species such as *Poa*, *Lolium* and *Agrostis* on which to lay their eggs. Dots on meadow brown hind-wings may trick birds into pecking at wings rather than at the vulnerable body. Females also have a second line of defence. If discovered, they quickly raise their fore-wings exposing gleaming eye spots which may frighten a predator away. Compared with most other species meadow browns spend relatively little time taking nectar from flowers, but when they do so bramble and thistles are often favoured.

Status and distribution:
This is probably the commonest butterfly of the area and is found in almost any grassy place.

RINGLET   *(Aphantopus hyperantus)*   Plate 12

Description:
The ground colour is dark brown, appearing almost black in males, which have an even darker area of scent scales across the fore-wings. Females are larger and paler with a row of more prominent eye spots near the wing-edges. The white-pupilled eye spots on the under-sides of both sexes are very conspicuous. In fresh specimens the white fringes to the wings are quite conspicuous.
In some individuals the eye-spots on the under-side are elongated rather than round, or they may be reduced to tiny white points (form *caeca*). In a more extreme (form *arete*), the eye markings are absent. Both forms have been seen at Friday Wood, Colchester. Albinism also occurs, with some, or all, of the wings white.

Similar Species:
In flight ringlets may resemble male meadow browns. In fresh specimens, the white
46

wing-fringes mark them out. Also, the plain grey-brown under-sides with prominent eye-markings of the ringlet are distinctive.

Life History:

The female scatters her buff-white, dome-shaped eggs among grasses. They hatch after two weeks or so. When full grown the larva is pale ochre brown with dark lines and a whitish lateral stripe. The surface is covered with fine hairs. The larva feeds until October on grasses including cock's foot (*Dactylis glomerata*), meadow grasses (*Poa spp.*) and false brome (*Brachypodium sylvaticum*), then goes into a partial hibernation, feeding during mild winter weather. It becomes full grown in June feeding only at night and remaining low down among the grass stems during the day. The pupa is pinkish-buff speckled and streaked with brown. It is formed on the ground at the base of grass and is attached. The butterfly hatches in about two weeks.

Habitat and Behaviour:

The butterfly is on the wing in July and August in grassy places, particularly in the rides and glades of woods and along hedges. Colonies are usually situated in damper, partially shaded areas of the woods, with lush growth of grasses. Flying mainly in July, the ringlet avoids the summer heat by living in woods and cool moist places where the air is damp and still. Male ringlets spend much of their time fluttering around grass heads and between tussocks in their search for mates. Both sexes spend long spells at flowers, jostling for nectar of brambles, thistles, knapweeds with meadow browns and gatekeepers. Numbers fluctuate according to weather conditions. For example after the long, hot summer of 1976 there was a serious reduction in some colonies but there was a rapid recovery during the cool, wet summers which followed.

Status and Distribution:

Edward Fitch, writing in 1891, stated: 'This very low-flying woodland butterfly is common throughout the county' and William Harwood, in 1903, merely wrote: 'Abundant and widely distributed'. Today, the butterfly remains quite widespread and well-established in North East Essex, though confined to suitable woodland habitats. Currently there are large colonies in Friday and Donyland Woods and at Markshall Estate, Coggeshall where one observer in 2000 estimated the numbers in July to be in the thousands.

SMALL HEATH (*Coenonympha pamphilus*)   Plate 13

Description:

The upper-side is pale tawny brown with a black spot near the tip of the fore-wing. The male has darkish borders, which are less noticeable in the female. The under-side of the hind-wings is grey marked with white, whilst the fore-wing under-sides are similar in colour and pattern to the upper-sides. Females are usually larger than the males. The smallest of the British species of the 'browns' (Satyrinae), with male wingspans at 33mm, females 37mm.

Life History:

There are two generations a year. The first is on the wing in May and June, the second in August and September. It overwinters as a young larva. May brood females lay their eggs singly on grass blades usually about 3cm above ground level. When first laid they are green but after a few days are ochre-brown with red-brown blotches. There are about 50 fine longitudinal keels. Eggs hatch after two weeks. Final instar larvae are green with whitish-green lines. Second brood females lay their eggs on grasses such as annual meadow grass (*Poa annua*), meadow fescue (*Festuca pratense*) and sheep's fescue (*Festuca ovina*). The second brood larvae hibernate and feed up in spring, producing the May/June generation. The pupa, suspended from a grass stem, is green with dark marks on the wing case. The butterfly hatches in about three weeks.

Habitat and Behaviour:

The butterfly inhabits open grassland, roadside verges and cart-tracks, coastal grazing marshes and wide woodland rides, usually on well-drained soils. Relatively short grass is preferred, dominated by the finer-leaved species on which the eggs are laid. The butterflies rest with wings closed, and so only the under-sides are visible. They are relatively inactive.

Status and Distribution:

Widespread and still fairly common in our area (though in unusually low numbers in spring 2002). There are flourishing colonies on (and behind) sea walls at East Mersea; Tollesbury Wick; Old Hall Marsh Nature Reserve; the Naze at Walton and Goldhanger and in the grassy areas next to borrowdykes at these sites. There is also a large colony in the grassland at Copt Hall, Little Wigborough (National Trust).

Chapter 3   MIGRATORY SPECIES

The butterfly population of North Essex is regularly reinforced by migrant species which arrive each year in spring and through the summer months from continental Europe and North Africa. Main visitors are the painted lady and red admiral with the clouded yellow appearing in varying numbers in most years. The pale clouded yellow and Camberwell beauty arrive only in some years when their populations in Europe are at high levels and when there are attempts to extend their range. In the case of the painted lady and the clouded yellows, although immigrant females lay eggs and these go on to produce adults later in the year, the species cannot survive our winters. There is increasing evidence that adult red admiral butterflies are hibernating successfully, though in small numbers, and the species still relies on immigration.

BATH WHITE (*Pontia daplidice*)

This very rare migrant could be confused with the female orange tip. Points of difference are: (a) the black area around the tip of the upper-side fore-wing white spots in it in the case of the Bath white, and (b) the black discal spot is larger than that of the female orange tip and has white in it; (c) the green markings on the under-side hind-wing of the bath white are much more evenly coloured and regular in shape. There was a sizable invasion of this species into Britain in 1945 and a smaller influx from southern Europe, where it is common, in 1947 but there were no records from Essex. In Victorian times specimens were captured at Stanway and Berechurch. (*Fitch 1891, Harwood 1903*).

CLOUDED YELLOW (*Colias croceus*)   Plate 3

Description:
The ground-colour of the upper-sides is a rich orange-yellow, and there are wide black borders to the wings. In the males these are unbroken, except for inconspicuous yellow outlining of the veins. In the females the black borders are broken with a row of yellow spots. Both sexes have a black discal spot in the fore-wings, and a reddish-orange spot in the discal area of the hind-wings. The undersides are yellow, with a black discal spot on the fore-wing (as on the upper-side), and a variable row of black markings towards the outer edge of the wings. There is a silvery 'figure-of-eight' spot in the discal area on the hind-wing. There is a less common pale form of the female, *f. helice*, in which the ground colour is pale grey-green, darker on the hind-wing.

Similar Species:

In flight, the pattern of bright orange-yellow with black borders is unmistakable. The brimstone is a paler yellow without black markings. Berger's clouded yellows are a bright lemon-yellow in the males, and quite distinctive. However, there could be confusion between form *helice* of the clouded yellow and the females of the paler Berger's clouded yellow. If a good view in flight is obtained, then the darker hind-wings of *helice* are distinctive.

Life History:

The clouded yellow does not usually survive the English winter, so the presence of this species in our area depends on the regular arrival of immigrants from further south in Europe. However, they do breed here through the spring and summer months, and into the autumn. The tall, slender flask-shaped eggs are laid on the leaves of plants in the Fabaceae (pea-family), especially clovers (*Trifolium spp.*), lucerne (*Medicago sativa*), and trefoils (*Lotus spp.*), often on cultivated land. The full-grown caterpillar is green with a pale yellow stripe down each side, and the chrysalis is yellow-green, hidden among the foliage.

Habitat and Behaviour:

As a migratory species, the clouded yellow tends to be seen flying rapidly over the countryside, occasionally stopping to take nectar from flowers such as clovers or thistles. But they sometimes congregate in areas where their larval food-plants are plentiful, and in former times were most frequently seen in clover and lucerne fields.

Occurrences in North East Essex:

A few clouded yellows are reported in our district in most years, but there are occasional years of greater abundance. The pale female form, *f. helice* is also occasionally seen. According to Rayner, both clouded yellows and pale clouded yellows were abundant in 1875 in the Maldon district, and form *helice* of the clouded yellow was seen at Hazeleigh in 1877. Fitch listed many scattered 19th century records from our area, noting 1877 as a year of exceptional abundance. In this year the 'white variety of the female' (*helice*) was also common, and there was an additional sighting of it at Colchester by Harwood in 1858. Looking back on the invasion-year of 1877, Harwood recalled that the clouded yellow was the commonest butterfly throughout the county. It had also been fairly common in 1892 and 1900. Cole saw them at East and West Mersea on June 9th 1892, and then as many as thirty in clover fields at East Mersea in August of that year. In September two *f. helice* were observed. 1949 was another clouded yellow year, when they were described as 'rampant in every field', especially lucerne, in the Clacton area. Dewick counted 1075 clouded yellows, together with 29 of the form *helice* from the Bradwell area in the 1949 season. 1983 and 1986 were also remarkable 'invasion' years, as was 2000. In that year the first arrivals were in May and early June, and they were seen at West Bergholt, Markshall, Copt Hall, East

Mersea and Tollesbury. Eggs were laid on lucerne, clover and bird's-foot trefoil and the resulting offspring were flying plentifully from August until mid-September. Dougal Urquart reported some 34 seen on various dates through the year at East Mersea, and there were reports of 25 at Jaywick (J. Young), 67 at Martin's Farm, St. Osyth (R. W. Arthur) and 79 at Bradwell-on-Sea (S. F. Dewick). The form *helice* was reported from East Mersea, Tollesbury and Walton.
(*Rayner 1884, Fitch 1891, Cole, Essex Naturalist 1892 (various notes), Harwood 1903, Seabrook Essex Naturalist 28, 1951, p.211, Dewick 1951, Firmin 1984, Goodey 1997, Firmin 2001, Urquhart, 2001, Goodey 2001*)

PALE CLOUDED YELLOW   (*Colias hyale*)
BERGER'S CLOUDED YELLOW   (*Colias alfacariensis*)

Description:
Both species have bright, lemon-yellow ground colour with broken black borders in the male upper-sides. The females are pale grey-green, also with broken black borders. Both sexes have a black discal spot in each fore-wing and a double orange spot in the discal area of the hindwing. The under-sides are similar to those of the clouded yellow, but generally paler yellow, especially on the central area of the under-side fore-wings. The adults of the two species are indistinguishable in the field, and can only be separated by dissection, although the caterpillars are markedly different. For differences between these species and the clouded yellow see under clouded yellow.

Life History:
Like the clouded yellow, these species are generally unable to survive our winters, so ones seen here are either migrants or descendants of migrants from earlier in the season. The larvae of the pale clouded yellow feed on Fabaceae such as clovers (*Trifolium spp.*) and lucerne (*Medicago sativa*), like the clouded yellow, but the larval food-plant of Berger's clouded yellow is typically horseshoe vetch (*Hippocrepis comosa*), a plant of chalk and limestone downs.

Occurrences in North East Essex:
The two species were only distinguished from each other in 1947 (on the basis of their different life-histories), so that literature records from before this date for the pale clouded yellow could refer to either species. However, there have so far been no confirmed records for Berger's clouded yellow from our area. The pale clouded yellow has always been a much scarcer and more irregular migrant than the clouded yellow, but, especially in the 19th century it had occasional years of relative abundance. Rayner reported it, along with the clouded yellow, as 'abundant' in 1875 and Fitch cited several such occurrences: forty one, St. Osyth, 1842; thirty six, Colchester, 1857; and seventy, Hazeleigh, 1875. Harwood added 1868, and 1900. In the latter year it was more common than the clouded ellow and 'probabl occurred in larger or smaller

numbers in every clover and lucerne field in the county'. From 1944 to 1951 it was common on the Essex coast, especially in the Dengie peninsula. One was seen at Copford on 4th September 1952. Since then the only definite records are from 1971 and 1983 on the Dengie peninsula.
(*Rayner 1884, Fitch 1891, Harwood 1903, Dewick 1951, Firmin et al. 1975, Emmet & Pyman 1983*)

LONG-TAILED BLUE   (*Lampides boeticus*)

Description:
The upper-side of the male is purplish blue. At the anal angle of the hind-wing are two black spots and a short black, white-tipped tail. Females are brownish-black and similarly marked with the bases of the wings shaded blue. The under-side is distinctive: pale brown marked with white lines and with two metallic-ringed black spots at the base of the tail. Wingspan: male 34mm; female 36mm.

Life History:
It may on occasion breed here but its larvae cannot survive an English winter. A favoured larval food plant is the everlasting pea (*Lathyrus latifolius*) and clumps of this common garden flower should be examined in summer for signs of larvae on the flowers or the young green pods.

Occurrences in North East Essex:
This is a rare immigrant to Britain though in fact one of the most widely distributed Lycaenids ('blues') in the world. Its nearest localities to Britain are in the Mediterranean region. There are so far only two confirmed records for North East Essex. A female was captured by R.W. Clamp in a lane close to the River Stour at Dedham in July, 1931. It was one of a small group of blue butterflies fluttering around a flowering plant of everlasting pea (*report in the Entomologist, Vol. 64, 1931*). A second record, also of a female, was of one settled on a flower of antirrhinum at Walton-on-the-Naze on 1 Oct. 1932. (*Entomologist 64, p. 179; Entomologist 65, p. 259*)

CAMBERWELL BEAUTY   (*Nymphalis antiopa*)   Plate 9

Description:
This large and striking immigrant from northern Europe has the upper-side of the wings chocolate brown with a straw-coloured margin. Just inside this border is a line of pale blue spots. The under-side is similar but without the blue spots. Wingspan: male 74mm; female 84mm.

Occurrences in North East Essex:

The Camberwell beauty gets its common name from the fact that the first recorded British specimen was captured at Camberwell, then a London village, in 1748. It is an occasional vagrant which periodically arrives in large numbers, as in 1976 and 1995. Old entomologists called it 'The Grand Surprise'. Jermyn reported it from Little Oakley, and there were occasional later sightings, with a significant 'invasion' in 1872, when William H. Harwood reported twelve from Colchester, with others reported from Maldon, Mundon, Witham, Halstead and Bradwell in the same year. A a single specimen was taken at Middlewick, Colchester in 1880 (by W. Tillaney). Subsequent reports include one from Colchester in 1952, and another seen by F.V. Duckworth flying round some willows in the garden of his home at Heathfields, Old Heath in September, 1958. During the late summer of 1976 there was the largest invasion of Camberwell beauties in Britain for more than a century when many hundreds crossed the North Sea. In Essex there were 14 sightings, the largest number ever recorded in the county to that date. The first 1976 record for North East Essex was from Chappel on August 17 when Mrs. G.M. Heaney of Colchester Road saw one feeding with other Vanessid butterflies on a buddleia bush in the driveway to her home. On August 21 Malcolm McVail of Parsons Heath, Colchester saw a Camberwell beauty basking on a log in his garden and it was again present on August 22. On August 22 Mr. R.W. Tickner saw and photographed an *antiopa* on a buddleia bush in his garden at Orchard Road, Alresford. On August 24 Alan Whitworth of Wix Lodge, Wix had close views of another flying along a lane on his farm. By a remarkable coincidence Mr. Whitworth's father saw (and photographed) another Camberwell beauty while on holiday in Pembrokeshire on August 31. This was the most westerly record for the 1976 invasion while his son's at Wix was the most easterly. There was one further report in 1977 (Alresford) and another in 1984 (West Mersea). On August 2, 1995 a Camberwell beauty was found feeding on the blooms of a white variety of buddleia, in a garden at Wordsworth Avenue, Maldon, by Mrs. Maureen Patient. It stayed for three days. This specimen was one of many reported from the area between Great Yarmouth in the north of the eastern region to Sussex in the south. One was watched feeding on a fallen apple in a garden at Lawford in August, 1995. On September 13, 1996 Ian Rose saw another in his garden at Mistley. In the winter of 1995/6 a hibernating Camberwell beauty was found in a shed in the Cambridge area and on April 5, 1996 another which had probably hibernated was watched in gardens in Chapel Lane, Hadleigh near Southend. Goodey (1997) gives more 1996 records.

(Jermyn 1827, Fitch 1891, Harwood 1903, Friedlein 1956, Firmin et al. 1975, Emmet & Pyman 1985, Goodey 1996, Goodey 1997)

PAINTED LADY (*Vanessa cardui*)   Plate 9

Description:
The upper-side ground colour is tawny-orange with a pink flush, and there are black markings. The fore-wing has several white marks towards the apex and on the hind-wings are two blue marks at the anal angle. The under-side fore-wing is similar to the upper-side and the hind-wing is patterned with ochre, white, olive-green and blue. Wingspan: male 65mm; female 66mm.

Life History:
The painted lady is an annual migrant to Britain from southern Europe and North Africa. The first immigrants are usually seen in late May and June. Females lay their small, green eggs on thistles. The newly hatched larva spins a silken shelter on the underside of a thistle leaf feeding on the lower cuticle. It continues to spin new tents until the last stage (instar) when it feeds in the open. When fully grown the larva's body is black with yellow markings, with a yellow stripe along the side. Spines are black or yellowish. The pupa is attached by tail hooks to a pad of silk and is formed in a tent-like structure similar to the larval shelter. It is greyish-brown marked with brown and metallic gold splashes. The butterfly hatches in two weeks.

Habitat and Behaviour:
The painted lady is a frequent visitor to gardens attracted by the nectar of flowers. It has a strong, swift flight and the male has a territory which it patrols, returning to settle on the same spot.

Status and Distribution:
There are one to two generations a year but the brood which emerges in August and September cannot sustain itself and adults or larvae are killed by cold weather in autumn and winter. Painted ladies continue to fly long after most butterflies have settled down for the night. Some obviously behave like moths and are on the wing in the hours of darkness. During a large immigration of painted ladies in 1980 an entomologist running a light trap on the east coast found 10 in his trap one morning in July. Some British-born painted ladies undertake a return migration in September and early October. They head south through mountain passes in the Alps and Pyrenees. In this way a reservoir of breeding stock is maintained in North Africa and countries bordering the Mediterranean.

Notable Immigrations:
The most memorable mass invasion of the post-war period was in 1996 when it is estimated that millions flew north from southern Spain and North Africa to western Europe and the British Isles. Some idea of the scale of the invasion in June, 1995, can be gauged from the observations of Ian Rose at Mistley. He estimated that between 11am

and 3pm on June 7 a minimum of 60 painted ladies every hour passed through his large garden in School Lane flying northwards on what was obviously a purposeful flight line. Many stopped to nectar on garden flowers before resuming flight. At Bradwell-on-Sea, Bob and Stephen Dewick, who have a nature reserve at Curry Farm, reported that hundreds of female painted ladies laid eggs on a hectare or so of thistles and this resulted in an estimated half a million larvae. Thousands of butterflies emerged from the glistening chrysalids. The other notable immigration was in 1980 when many thousands arrived in two waves in June and July.

RED ADMIRAL (*Vanessa atalanta*)   Plate 8

Description:

The upper-side is black and the fore-wing has a scarlet band, white blotches near the apex and a trace of blue on the margin. In some specimens a white dot may be present in the scarlet band. The hind-wing has a band of scarlet along the margin with black dots. There are blue marks at the anal angle. The hind-wings are beautifully mottled with brown, bronzy-green and black. On the costal margin is a big, cream-coloured blotch. Wingspan: male 67mm; female 72mm.

Life History:

Females lay their eggs on stinging nettle (*Urtica dioica*) leaves. These are green and small with 10 prominent glassy keels. They are laid singly on the upper surface of the nettle leaves and hatch in a week. On hatching the young larva goes to the base of a young leaf where it makes a tent by pulling the edges of the leaf together with silk. As it grows the larva constructs larger tents in which it rests in a 'J' shape. When full grown after the fourth moult it is black speckled with white and yellow spines and marks along the sides. There are also grey-green forms marked with yellow-green or brown, with black spines or yellowish spines. The pupa is greyish marked with gold and is suspended by tail hooks from a pad of silk inside its last larval tent. It hatches after two weeks.

Habitat and Behaviour:

This common and widespread species is found in almost any kind of habitat but in late summer and autumn the offspring of the spring invaders are most frequently seen in gardens where they nectar on buddleia, michaelmas daisies, dahlias and sedums. Ivy bloom is also attractive and so is the juice from over-ripe or fallen fruit. Also irresistible is the fermenting sap oozing from tree scars.

Distribution and Status:

The red admiral is a migrant species reaching England in spring from southern Europe. In the mild winters of recent years, numbers of red admirals have hibernated in Britain, giving rise to sightings in January and February on sunny days. As with the painted lady there is a partial return migration to southern Europe in autumn.

QUEEN OF SPAIN FRITILLARY   (*Argynnis lathonia*)

This is a rare migrant to Britain, but in the last decade it was increasingly seen in eastern counties with possible breeding in east Suffolk. The upper-side is orange brown spotted with black. The large silver spots on the under-side of the hind-wings will prevent confusion with other resident fritillaries (wingspan: male 46mm; female 52mm).

The species is common in southern Europe and there are colonies in the coastal dunes across the North Sea in Holland and Denmark. The larvae feed on field pansies (*Viola arvensis* and *V. tricolor*). One was seen near Colchester in 1818, and Jermyn reported it from Stoke-by-Nayland. Both Harwood and Fitch reported several specimens seen during the later years of the 19th century: five, Colchester, 1857; one, Colchester 1858; two, Colchester 1868; one, St. Osyth 1881. Two were seen in Colchester in 1918, after which there were no further reports until 1995. Sightings in that year coincided with an invasion of Camberwell beauties from Scandinavia. Queen of Spains were seen at Bradwell-on-Sea; Landermere (Walton Backwaters); Thorrington and Kelvedon, all in August.

(*Jermyn 1827, Fitch 1891, Newman 1871, Harwood 1903, Goodey 1996, Corke 1997*)

Chapter 4   THE LOST ONES

The butterflies described in this chapter were once to be found in the Colchester area and North East Essex but were lost as resident species in the 19th and 20th centuries. It is hoped that under Biodiversity Action Plans some of them may be successfully reintroduced.

DINGY SKIPPER   (*Erynnis tages*)   Plate 2

Description:
Like the other 'skippers', this is a small butterfly (wing-span 30 mm.). Though its ground-colour is medium to dark brown on the upper-side, its common name is definitely misleading. Both fore- and hind-wings are medium brown, with darker, broken and irregular bands across the fore-wings. Between these darker bands and sometimes round the wing-margins there often are splashes and spots of white scaling. In some specimens this produces an intricate and eye-catching pattern of contrasts. In this species, as in the grizzled skipper, the scent scales are contained in a narrow flap formed by the rolling back of the leading edge of the fore-wings. This is quite noticeable, especially in older, worn specimens, and is, of course, absent in the females. The under-sides are pale, light brown with one or more rows of faintly marked lighter spots towards or around the wing-margins.

Life History:
The eggs, which are bright orange, and dome-shaped, are laid on the upper-sides of the leaves of the larval food-plant. In North East Essex, this was invariably bird's-foot trefoil (*Lotus corniculatus*), though it also feeds on horseshoe vetch (*Hippocrepis comosa*) in its more favoured chalk and limestone localities elsewhere. The eggs soon hatch, and the resulting caterpillars feed under the shelter of a loose 'tent' formed from leaves until, full-grown, they begin hibernation in late July. Pupation takes place the following spring, and the butterflies emerge in May, continuing to fly into June. In favourable years there is a small second generation which flies in August.

Habitat and Behaviour:
Sheltered but sunny grassland and heaths, especially where these have a south-facing slope, wide woodland rides, disused quarries and railway cuttings are among the favoured habitats of this species. Recent research has shown that this butterfly requires large areas of appropriately managed habitat. Areas of bare ground are required for colonisation by the bird's-foot trefoil, but the butterfly also requires more sheltered areas with more rank vegetation for shelter and roosting. Heavy grazing is also damaging, in removing the taller shoots of the food-plant on which the eggs are laid. Low-level rotational grazing is recommended (*Asher et al. 2001*).

History:

The dingy skipper seems to have become extinct in the Colchester area in or around 1990. This population seems to have been the last one to survive in Essex. The early entomologists did not regard it as a common species. According to Fitch it was not common in Essex, and as far as the North East was concerned, it had been taken once (by a Mr. Tillaney) at Langham Lodge Wood, 'nearly 30 years ago'. Harwood had never seen it alive. Just to the west of our area, Weeks recorded it on Lingwood Common. Harwood (1903), cited Mathew as saying it occurred near Harwich and Harwood himself had found several in High Woods in 1893. Since then it had become quite common. Subsequent records include Woodham Mortimer in 1946, West Bergholt, Fingringhoe, Marks Tey, Stanway, Berechurch, Danbury and Hilly Fields, Colchester. However, from the late 1960s it rapidly declined, so that by the beginning of the 1980s the only remaining known colonies in our part of the county were on the M.oD. lands to the south of Colchester. Former habitats have been lost through lack of management and encroachment by rank vegetation and scrub, whilst others have been lost to agricultural intensification. The decline of the species in North East Essex coincided with a much wider process of decline throughout its range in the rest of England, most pronounced away from its chalk and limestone strongholds. The extensive colony on M.o.D. land south of Colchester was closely monitored in the 1980s until its demise around 1990. The species was thinly distributed in five one-kilometre squares, on heathland both east and west of Friday wood, with a particularly strong population on rides through a new oak plantation at the eastern edge of the wood. The rides ran north-south and were both sheltered and sunny, with an abundance of bird's-foot trefoil (*Lotus corniculatus*). However, the rides were not managed, and eventually became overshaded as the trees grew, leading to the extinction of the species in this part of its habitat. A small population of the species survived for a few more years in one corner of a rough meadow in the same general area, but this too became overgrown. Searches in 1992 and 1993 proved fruitless, and the species in now presumed extinct in North East Essex, as it is in the whole county.

(*Fitch 1891, Weeks Essex Naturalist 9, 1896, p. 261, Harwood 1903, Laidlaw Essex Naturalist 28, 1951, p. 78, Firmin et al. 1975, Benton 1982, 1983, Goodey & Firmin 1992, Firmin 1995a, Corke 1997*)

This species is still widespread on both the North and South Downs, and there are a few scattered colonies in the Norfolk Brecks (*see Watts & McIlwrath 2002*)

GRIZZLED SKIPPER (*Pyrgus malvae*)   Plate 2

Description:

Like the other 'skippers', a small butterfly (wing-span approximately 27mm.), with a brightly contrasting black-and-white chess-board pattern on the wings. The fringes are 'laddered' alternating black and white, and the males have their scent-scales hidden in a fold formed by the rolling-back of the leading edge of the fore-wings (as in the dingy skipper). The undersides are a dull grey-brown, with a pattern of white markings similar to that on the upper-side, and with the veins outlined yellowish.

Similar Species:
There are thirteen other species belonging to this group of skippers in the rest of Europe, and they can be very difficult to tell apart. Luckily (!) this is the only one we have in Britain, and it could not be confused with any other British butterfly. However, there is a small, grey and black day-flying moth, the mother shipton (*Euclidia mi*) which resembles the grizzled skipper when in flight, and can be found in similar habitats. But the distinctive wing-pattern (resembling the profile of a face, with protruding chin and nose) of the moth is quite distinctive when a close view is obtained.

Life History:
The eggs, which are dome-shaped and pale, whitish in colour, are laid singly on the leaves of the larval food-plants. These are normally wild strawberry (*Fragaria vesca*) or creeping cinquefoil (*Potentilla repens*), but several other members of the Rosaceae, such as barren strawberry (*Potentilla sterilis*) can be used. The caterpillars feed on the leaves of the food-plant, living in 'tents' formed by spinning together leaves with silk threads. When full-grown the caterpillar is dark green with brown longitudinal stripes and a black head. It pupates in a loose cocoon and hibernates through the winter in this stage. The butterflies emerge in May and fly through June, with an occasional small second generation later in the season.

Habitat and Behaviour:
The butterfly is often common on chalk and limestone down-land, but in our area it used to occur in open, sunny woodland rides and clearings, patches of unimproved grassland, railway banks and dry heath-land slopes. It requires a mosaic of short, sparsely vegetated grassland and taller, rank vegetation and scrub-edge, with abundant nectar sources in the spring, and an adequate supply of the larval food-plants. The adult butterflies have a low, swift flight, so that their movements are often difficult to follow. They bask in the sunshine with wings fully spread out, facing the sun, but close their wings when disturbed.

History:
It is almost certainly now extinct in North East Essex. Jermyn gave Hartley Wood as a locality for this species. According to Fitch it was common throughout Essex, but local and not easily seen or caught. For to Harwood it was common and widely distributed in many places. Laidlaw listed it for Woodham Mortimer in 1946. Clark and Hobday, reporting on their 1963 survey, list it as reported from Colchester, and noted one specimen from Frinton. Firmin et al. reported a 'drastic decline' since Harwood's day, but still thought its localities too numerous to list. By the time of Emmet & Pyman (1985) further decline was evident, through habitat destruction or deterioration, so that only the Colchester population

continued to exist in the North East of the county. This was present at low density on the same areas of M.o.D. heath-land as the dingy skipper, and was also monitored closely during the 1980s. A survey carried out by Benton and Barnham in May and June 1982 located very small numbers of the species in just three one-kilometre squares. They flew together with the dingy skipper in a small oak plantation on the edge of Friday Wood in the 1980s, but died out as the rides became overgrown and shaded by the growing trees. They survived a little later in a nearby scrubby meadow, which was selected for habitat management, but soon became extinct here, too. The last to be recorded was a singleton in 1991. The species is now almost certainly extinct in North East Essex, its decline to extinction here being consistent with the wider pattern of retraction to its strongholds in central and southern counties of England observed in recent decades. It remains to be seen whether planned re-introductions in suitable localities will be successful.

(*Jermyn 1827, Fitch 1891, Harwood 1903, Laidlaw Essex Naturalist 28, 1951, p.78, Firmin et al. 1975, Benton 1982, 1983, Emmet & Pyman 1985, Goodey & Firmin 1992, Corke 1997, Asher et al. 2001*)

The butterfly may still be seen at the Langdon Meadows Nature Reserve, in South Essex.

WOOD WHITE   (*Leptidea sinapis*)

Description:
Very small and delicate, compared to the other members of the 'white' family (*Pieridae*). The upper-sides are white in both sexes, with a squarish black tip to the fore-wings in the males, and a more diffuse, greyish one in the females. The under-side hind-wings are pale yellow with variable, obscure grey-green banding. There is an occasional second generation in summer, in which the ground colour of the hind-wings is usually paler, and the black tip to the fore-wings of the male more dense.

Similar Species:
In continental Europe two other wood-white species have traditionally been recognised: Fenton's (*L. morsei*) and the Eastern (*L. duponcheli*). Neither of these species is at all likely to be met with in North East Essex, but very recently a fourth species has been distinguished. This is *Leptidea reali*. It often flies together with the common wood white, and it can only be distinguished from the latter by dissection of the male genitalia! So far, *L. reali* has not been proved to exist in England, but it remains a possibility.

Life History:
The butterfly is usually on the wing from late May through June. The eggs are laid singly on the leaves or stems of the larval food-plant. This is most commonly yellow vetchling (*Lathyrus pratensis*), but often other Fabaceae - such as tufted vetch (*Vicia*

60

cracca) or bird's-foot trefoils (*Lotus spp.*) - are used. The caterpillars feed during the summer, and when full grown are green with a yellow stripe down each side. They leave the food-plant to pupate among rank vegetation, and spend the winter in the chrysalis stage.

Habitat and Behaviour:

As the name implies, this is typically a woodland butterfly, although it can sometimes be found along old hedgerows and field margins. In woods, wide, sunny and sheltered rides, clearings, or young plantations are its favoured haunts. As new plantations develop and become more shaded, colonies of the wood white die out, so they are dependent on felling or active ride-management. The butterflies have a weak, fluttering flight, usually staying close to the scrub or woodland edge, and occasionally stopping to take nectar from a flower or, in the case of the females, to lay eggs on a prominent patch of the vetchling. When at rest, nectaring or egg-laying, they keep their wings closed, so that the upper-side characters can only be seen in flight. They have a complex and fascinating courtship display, involving repeated 'flashing' of the white patches on the under-sides of the tips of their antennae. The male and female face each other during the display, and also unfurl their proboses to probe between one-another's fore-wings. Interestingly, the white patch is absent in the close European relative, the eastern wood white, with which the wood white often flies in southern Europe.

History:

The wood white is currently extinct in North East Essex, and, indeed, in the whole of Essex. It seems that it was already extinct by the time Harwood wrote his contribution to the Victoria County History, but there were several noted sites for it in our area in the 19th century. These included: Stour and Hartley Woods and Bromley Thickets; Donyland Heath; Markshall Woods, near Coggeshall and Witham. According to Harwood, Dr. Maclean had reported it to have been common in several woods near Colchester in the early 19th century.
(*Jermyn 1827, Fitch 1891, Harwood 1903*)
The butterfly has declined considerably in England since the1980s, and the nearest places to find it are in Buckinghamshire and Northamptonshire woods.

BROWN HAIRSTREAK (*Thecla betulae*)

Description:

Relatively large for a hairstreak, the brown hairstreak has dark brown upper-sides, with distinct 'tails' projecting from the rear edge of the hind-wings. There is a dark cell-spot, and a wide orange band on the fore-wings of the females, much reduced in the males. The undersides are a rich golden brown, with a white 'hairstreak' across fore and hind-wings, and a second white line across part of the hind wing.

Life History:
The white eggs are laid on twigs of low-growing blackthorn (*Prunus spinosa*) shrubs, usually between one and two metres from the ground. They over-winter in this stage and are quite conspicuous. The green caterpillars hatch in early spring and begin feeding on the opening buds of the blackthorn. It continues to feed on leaves until late June or July, when it falls to the ground and pupates. The butterfly emerges from late July and may continue to fly through September and into early October.

Habitat and Behaviour:
Typical colonies are associated with blackthorn hedges or woodland edges. The adult butterflies congregate around mature trees, referred to as 'master' trees. The males tend to remain close to these trees but the females disperse to lay their eggs. In poor weather they remain motionless, wings closed, but bask, wings half-open, in sunshine. Like other hairstreaks, they feed on aphid honeydew on leaves, but sometimes will come down to nectar from such flowers as bramble and hemp agrimony. The males are seen much more rarely.

History:
Hedgerow removal and the abandonment of traditional hedgerow management in favour of mechanical flailing have led to major declines in large parts of its UK range, especially in lowland east and central England, but this would not explain its early extinction from North East Essex. This species was present here in woods near Maldon, either side of the Ipswich road, close to the Suffolk border, and in and around High Woods, Colchester, in the early decades of the 19th century. It presumably died out some time before 1860 around Colchester, and Huggins searched the Maldon localities in the early 1950s, without success. There have been no subsequent reliable records for our area. The reasons for its extinction are unknown, and predate the agricultural changes responsible for the current loss of colonies elsewhere in England. It persisted in Suffolk until the 1940s, and in Kent until the 1970s.
(*Jermyn 1827, Raynor 1884, Fitch 1891, Harwood 1903, Huggins 1956, Asher et al. 2001*)
The nearest places to find the species now are wooded areas of the west Weald of Surrey and West Sussex.

DUKE OF BURGUNDY (*Hamearis lucina*)

Description:
This butterfly has the superficial appearance of a small fritillary, but is placed in a separate family (Riodinidae), of which it is the only European species. The upper-side is brownish-black marked with tawny orange bands broken up into spots. The wing-fringes are white, chequered black. The under-side fore-wings are similar in colour and pattern to the upper-sides, but the under-side hind-wings are mainly orange with

two bands of large white spots. Wingspan 29mm.

Life History:

The transparent eggs are laid on the underside of the leaves of cowslip (*Primula veris*) or primrose (*Primula vugaris*) in May or June. The full-grown caterpillar is grey-brown and very hairy. It feeds at night. The winter is spent in the pupal stage, and the adult butterfly emerges in May.

Habitat and Behaviour:

The Duke of Burgundy has two main habitats - chalk or limestone grassland and open, coppiced woodland. It seems likely that in the 19th century the latter was its main habitat in England, and this would have been the case in North East Essex. Cessation of coppice management is thought to have been the main reason for the drastic decline of woodland colonies of this species in the 20th century. In its woodland habitat the eggs are laid on large-leaved primrose plants, growing in warm but partly shaded areas. The males are strongly territorial.

History:

Jermyn reported it from her favoured Essex localities, Bromley Thickets and Hartley Wood, whilst according to Raynor it was common but local in Woodham Ferrers Hall Wood. William Harwood, writing in 1903, described it as uncommon and local. He added: 'However it is sometimes met with in several woods in the Tendring Hundred'. Gervase Mathew submitted a single report from the Harwich area in 1911. There are no reliable subsequent reports, and the species has almost certainly been extinct in our area for the past century.
(*Jermyn 1827, Raynor 1884, Harwood 1903, Corke 1997*)
There are small remaining colonies in Kent, but the nearest localities for reliable sightings of this butterfly are in the Chilterns and Berkshire Downs.

PURPLE EMPEROR (*Apatura iris*)   Plate 8

Description:

This large and beautiful species is often considered to be the finest of Britain's woodland butterflies. The male has a beautiful purple iridescence on the upper-side of its wings, which are marked with white spots and lines. At the anal angle of each hind-wing is a tawny mark and a black spot with a tawny surround. The female is larger than the male with a browner ground colour, slightly larger white markings and completely lacks the purple colouring. In both sexes the white markings on the under-side are similar to those above. The ground colour is shades of reddish-brown and pinkish grey, with a large eye spot on the fore-wing. Average wingspan of the male is 75mm; female 84mm.

Life History:

The eggs are 1mm tall, and bluntly conical in shape and green with a purplish base. They are laid on the upper-side of sallow (*Salix spp.*) leaves and hatch after a fortnight. When newly emerged the larva is greenish-yellow with a black head. After the first moult the ground colour is green with yellow side stripes and a yellow 'saddle' mark. The last segment has two anal points and the head has a pair of ochre-brown horns. When fully grown, after the fourth moult, the general shape is slug-like with a granular surface. The young larva begins hibernation after the second moult in October usually in the fork of a twig or a scar in the bark of the sallow bush or on a leaf which has been secured to the stem with silk. Feeding recommences in March. The pupa, in June and July, is suspended by tail hooks from a pad of silk attached to the underside of a sallow leaf. The pupa is very leaf-like, green and flattened in shape and marked with whitish lines which resemble the veins of a leaf. It hatches after about two weeks.

Habitat and Behaviour:

In Essex the purple emperor was found in oak-ash woodland often managed for game where the rides and glades were kept brushed clear enabling the butterflies space for courtship flights and also for feeding at puddles, on animal dung, or on the juices of decaying animal or bird carcasses. The purple emperor may escape notice because of its habit of soaring round the tops of tall oak and ash trees or resting on the highest leaves and twigs. But when it does leave its lofty perches its flight is strong and fast. It fearlessly chases other butterflies and even birds which venture into its chosen territory. Flowers do not seem to attract it but it comes readily to various noxious substances such as dung, carrion, the liquid from manure heaps and dirty puddles. It feeds from the honeydew left by aphids and also sucks up minerals in the wet patches in woodland paths and rides. The males are also attracted to shiny surfaces such as car windscreens and wheel hubs. The female, when intent on laying her eggs, flies into a sallow bush, generally disappearing from view.

History:

The purple emperor was believed by Harwood to have occurred in all the larger Essex woods in past times, but by the beginning of the 20th century it had become 'exceedingly rare' in its former North East Essex strongholds. Despite very occasional sightings, it is almost certainly extinct as a breeding species in our part of Essex and, very probably, in the county as a whole. In the 19th century it occurred in the woods between St Osyth and Weeley, in Stour and Copperas woods, on the Stour estuary, in High Woods, Colchester, the woods either side of the Ipswich road, north of Colchester (Birch and Langham Hall), and at Halstead and Coggeshall.

The earliest recorded British purple emperor was one captured in July, 1695, near Hedingham Castle by a Mr Courtman. This was given to the famous naturalist John Ray of Black Notley, the 'father' of British natural history, and is recorded in Ray's *Historia Insectorum* (1710). There are numerous references to the butterfly in North East Essex woodlands through the 19th century. Jermyn gave Great and Little Stour

Woods (the latter presumably the wood now known as Copperas) as localities. J.W. Douglas wrote in 1842 of a visit to Hartley and Riddles woods: 'between eighty and one hundred were seen performing their graceful and rapid evolutions about the tops of the oaks and aspens, gliding among the foliage.' Dr. Alan Maclean, the Colchester naturalist and physician, described the life history of the purple emperor from eggs and larvae found at High Woods, Colchester. He watched a female purple emperor deposit two eggs on the upper surfaces of two leaves of the sallow or great goat willow (*Salix caprea*) on July 15. The year is not given but it was probably in 1861. Maclean sent Edward Newman detailed descriptions of the various instars (stages) of the larva development including the hibernation on sallow twigs in winter, and these were used in Newman's *Illustrated Natural History of British Butterflies and Moths* (1870). Maldon Woods, near Weeley were evidently the hunting ground for 19th century collectors who used to hang up dead rabbits to lure male purple emperors from their lofty perches on the top branches of oaks. The big butterflies found the juices of the decaying rabbit carcasses irresistible. Doubleday found it commonly at Colchester in the mid 19th century, and Harwood informed Newman that it had been common in High Woods up to 1860 but had not been seen there or in the other woods near Colchester since. The last specimen taken had been flying round a moderator lamp in the town itself! The specimen, a female, was in the collection of Dr. Henry Laver, the Colchester physician and naturalist. However, the butterfly reappeared in the Colchester district and was again common in the early 1880s, only to decline again to become exceedingly rare by the end of the century.

The last fully authenticated specimen was one taken by Gervase F. Mathew, the retired Paymaster-in-Chief of the Royal Navy on July 6, 1893, probably in Stour Wood. This now historic specimen, the last authenticated for Essex, is in the reference collections at Colchester Museums. Despite occasional reports of sightings (e.g. near Weeley and at Colchester in the 1950s, Wivenhoe in 1983) in the 20th century, it seems very likely that the purple emperor was extinct in our area by the end of the first decade of the 20th century, at the latest. In Harwood's opinion, the annual clearance of underwood, involving cutting the sallow bushes on which the larvae were hibernating, was responsible for the demise of the purple emperor, along with the destruction of the woods themselves: 'For the green woods of England have disappeared in all directions, and their beautiful wild flowers, birds and insects have to a considerable extent gone with them'.

The purple emperor hung on in woodland at Raydon, near Hadleigh, Suffolk which is less than 20 miles from Colchester, until 1960 but unfortunately forestry changes, including the planting of conifers, destroyed the habitat for the purple emperor when most of the oaks and sallow bushes were felled.

(*Ray 1710, Jermyn 1827, Douglas 1842, Newman 1870, Newman 1871, Fitch 1891, Harwood 1903, Firmin et al. 1975, Goodey and Pyman 1983, Corke 1997, Colchester Museum Collections*)

It is hoped that the species can be reintroduced to some of the woods in North Essex under the Essex Biodiversity Action Plan once the suitability of the habitats has been carefully evaluated. The purple emperor can still be observed in some of the larger woods on the Weald of Surrey and Sussex.

LARGE TORTOISESHELL (*Nymphalis polychloros*)

Description:
The ground colour of the upper-side is brownish-orange, marked with black and yellowish ochre. The hind-wing has a marginal row of blue lunules and the antennae are tipped with yellow. The under-side is mottled with shades of brown and purple and the cell of the hind-wing contains a white dot. The sexes are similar but females are slightly larger. Average size of male wingspan 64mm; female 70mm.

Similar Species:
The large tortoiseshell may be distinguished from its smaller relative, the small tortoiseshell, by its larger size, paler orange colouring, absence of white on the forewing and the presence of seven black spots on the upperside forewing whereas the small tortoiseshell has only six. In the past when large tortoiseshells were flying after hibernation in spring there was occasional confusion among less-experienced observers between this species and the comma which has similar wing colouring but is smaller.

Life History:
The butterfly is (or was) on the wing from late June until September. Egg-laying takes place about two weeks after pairing. Eggs are laid in batches encircling twigs of elm (*Ulmus spp.*) or sallow (*Salix spp.*). The egg when first laid is yellowish-orange gradually darkening to amber brown. Each egg has about eight glassy longitudinal keels. The larva, after the fourth and last moult, has the head and body black and the body is speckled with white and marked with orange lines. The spines are yellowish-orange and sharp. The larvae live and feed gregariously in webs. In the later stages they dispense with the web but still keep close together. They are very vulnerable to attacks by parasitic wasps and flies. The pupa is suspended by tail hooks from a pad of silk, usually from foodplant twigs or leaves. It is pinkish brown in colour, marked with gold spots. The butterfly hatches after about two weeks.

Habitat and Behaviour:
The main haunts of this fine, big, fast-flying butterfly were the rides and glades of woods, roadways and lanes bordering woods and country roads where these are lined with elms and tall hedgerow growth. After hibernation the large tortoiseshell feeds on the blooms of sallow and other spring flowers and likes to bask on warm tree trunks with wings held wide apart. It hibernated through the winter in old sheds, barns, hollow trees and piles of timber stacked in woods. Pairing takes place in spring and the butterflies, freshly emerged from winter quarters, are fond of basking on dry, rutted

ground in woodland rides and glades and on the trunks of trees.

History:
The large tortoiseshell was once widely distributed in wooded areas and tree-lined lanes where elm trees abounded in north Essex and Suffolk but disappeared from the region, and elsewhere in eastern and southern Britain before the end of the 1950s. This coincided with the spread of Dutch elm disease; an abundance of parasitic ichneumon wasps which prey on larvae; hedgerow destruction in arable farm areas; and a succession of cold, wet springs and cool summers. The large tortoiseshell is now considered to be extinct as a resident species in Britain. Occasional coastal records in the past decade may be of immigrants or specimens which have been bred and released from Continental stock obtained from dealers.
Joe Firmin and the late Donald Blaxill may have seen some of the last Essex large tortoiseshells in a wood on the Markshall Estate, Coggeshall in April, 1954. They saw four in woodland rides sitting on patches of dried earth or basking on tree trunks. Two were watched nectaring on primrose blooms. One large tortoiseshell flew on to the remains of a stoat on a gamekeeper's gibbet and sat gently opening and shutting its wings in the warm spring sunshine. Large tortoiseshell populations were always subject to peaks and troughs. William H. Harwood commented on this in late Victorian times pointing out that in some years elm trees were covered with the webs of larvae while in others the larvae and adults were far from common. Harwood correctly instanced the devastating impact of ichneumon parasitism on the larval clusters when as many as 70 per cent were affected. Then there were years of contrasting superabundance. Writing in 1901 Harwood said:
'The caterpillars were so excessively abundant in north Essex and on the southern side of the River Stour that I could have taken hundreds of broods had I required them'. During the warm summers of the mid-1940s the Essex and Suffolk populations of the large tortoiseshell enjoyed a new upsurge and the species was again locally common, lasting until 1949. From then on numbers dipped and by the final years of the 1950s the species had disappeared from all its former strongholds. Blaxill in 1978 speculated on the reasons behind the dramatic decline in the species. He wrote: 'The species is prone to heavy parasitism by ichneumon wasps and I suspect that this, as well as climatic changes, has been the factor behind the disappearance of this fine butterfly after its period of comparative plenty soon after the second world war'. Blaxill went on to say that after many years of observation he was convinced that the large tortoiseshell should be classed as an immigrant which will hibernate under favourable conditions in certain areas and continue for a number of years following local colonisations. In Britain it is on the edge of its normal European range. The immigration thesis is reinforced by sightings in recent years in coastal areas of Essex, Suffolk, Kent and Sussex, but is disputed by expert lepidopterists such as Dr. Jeremy Thomas who points out that this species has not been recorded on lightships or other offshore vessels, as is the case with regular migrants. A large tortoiseshell was photographed by David Scott at Ford Farm, Brightlingsea on August 28, 1999, the eighth Essex record since 1990, most of

the others coming from the Dengie Peninsula. Another was photographed at Landguard Point, Felixstowe, Suffolk, on June 20, 2001.
On July 19,2002 Ian Rose found a specimen of the large tortoiseshell fluttering in one of the windows of his Mistley home, evidently having entered through an open window. Ian checked it in case it might have been a rare immigrant example of the yellow-legged tortoiseshell (*Nympalis xanthomelas*) which has occasionally been found on the English east coast as an immigrant from eastern Europe. Ian was satisfied that the specimen was, in fact, a large tortoiseshell and released it after taking colour photos. The origin of the specimen remains a mystery. The large tortoiseshell is not considered to be a migrant and as far as is known none of its former colonies in NE Essex and Suffolk have survived. It is now considered extinct as a resident British species. As some people rear and release large tortoisehells from larvae of Continental origin obtained from dealers it is possible that the Mistley specimen is one of these clandestine releases. However there is a remote possibility that a colony has survived somewhere in the Mistley/Lawford area and Ian's specimen could be a native 'survivor'.
However, the species is in decline in continental Europe, so prospects of its recovery in Britain appear slight.
(*Blaxill 1978, Thomas & Lewington 1991, Harwood 1903, Blaxill 1978, Firmin et al. 1975, Corke 1997, Asher et al. 2001*)

SMALL PEARL-BORDED FRITILLARY (*Boloria selene*)

Description:
The upperside is orange-brown marked with black and very similar to the pearl-bordered fritillary but distinguished by the darker colour on the upper-side and the presence of several more patches of silver on the under-side of the hind-wing.

Life History:
The larvae fed on the leaves of dog-violet (*Viola riviniana*), and possibly other species of violet. They feed during the summer and hibernate when nearly full-grown. They begin feeding again in spring, and the pupa is formed deep in vegetation. The butterfly emerges at the end of May or early June and can be seen on the wing throughout the month of June. In some years there is a smaller second brood which flies in August.

Habitat and Behaviour:
In southern Britain, the small pearl-bordered fritillary is to be found in open, coppiced woodland, wide woodland rides and heaths. The males fly close to the ground, in search of females, occasionally stopping to take nectar from brambles or thistles. Both sexes bask with open wings facing the sun in early evening.

History:
This butterfly was quite common and widespread in Essex during the 19th century.
68

Jermyn reported it from several of her favoured localities: Stour, Hartley and Hamlet's Woods, and Bromley Thickets. According to Raynor, writing of the mid 1870s and early 1880s, it was plentiful in Woodham Ferrers Hall Wood. Both Harwood and Fitch report it as common, and Harwood says 'sometimes abundant in flowery places in woods'. There is a specimen in Colchester Museum collections which was caught by Mathew on 7th June 1910, with the comment that it used to occur in Stour Wood. There are no subsequent records from North East Essex, and the species has probably been extinct here for almost a century. There is some evidence of its survival up to the 1950s elsewhere in the county, but since then it has disappeared not just from Essex but from much of South and Central England. The decline of coppicing, and the shading out of its woodland habitats is generally given as the main reason for the local extinction of the butterfly. It has fared rather better in parts of the South West and North West of England, Wales and Scotland, where it uses other habitats, such as coastal cliffs and damp moorland.
There remain a few colonies in the woods of the Sussex and Surrey Weald and in Hampshire.
(Jermyn 1827, Raynor 1884, Fitch 1891, Harwood 1903, Colchester Museum collections, Thomas 1986, Corke 1997, Asher et al. 2001)

PEARL-BORDERED FRITILLARY (*Clossiana euphrosyne*)

Description:

The upper-side is orange-brown marked with black. On the under-side of the hind-wings are two sliver patches and a marginal row of silver lunules. Females are slightly larger and more yellowish than the males, the pale marginal markings on the upper-side of the hind-wing are more prominent and the wings more rounded. Male wingspan 44mm; female 47mm.

Life History:

The butterflies are on the wing from mid-May until mid-June (overlapping, but a little earlier than the small pearl-bordered fritillary). The eggs are laid singly on leaf-litter or stones near to the violets, or sometimes on stems or leaves of dog-violet (*Viola riviniana*) or heath dog-violet (*Viola canina*). The eggs are whitish in colour with 20 to 25 longitudinal keels and hatch after two weeks. When newly hatched the larva is brown with transverse bands and covered with fine hairs. The head is shining black. After the second moult the body colour becomes almost black and the hairs are black and spiny. When fully grown after the fourth moult the body is black and covered with conical spines and the two dorsal rows have yellowish bases. Larvae go into hibernation at the beginning of August after the third moult, usually inside dead or curled up leaves. Feeding recommences in March and the larvae feed by day, leaving the foodplant at night. The pupa hangs from a pad of silk spun on a leaf stem on or near the foodplant. It is brown and resembles a dead leaf. The butterfly emerges after about 10 days.

Habitat and Behaviour:

The favoured haunts of this attractive spring butterfly are the clearings of woods where the undergrowth has been cut down for two or three years, and the ground is carpeted with wild flowers such as bluebell, bugle, violet and primrose. In these sunlit glades and rides the butterflies fly rapidly to and fro, the flight being graceful, swift and gliding. Towards evening it likes to bask with wings expanded in the lowering sunshine, resting on the ground or foliage.

History:

Jermyn lists this species from the same localities as for the last: Stour, Hartley and Hamlet's Woods and Bromley Thickets. Raynor adds Woodham Ferrers Hall Wood and Danbury, whilst Fitch and Harwood both thought it more common than the last species, and widely distributed in its woodland habitats. There are specimens, probably from Stour Wood, collected by Mathew, in May 1906 and June 1907 and 8 in Colchester Museum collections. However, Harwood noted the tendency of populations of both species to fluctuate, with periods of unusual abundance followed by relative scarcity. It is perhaps ironic that the famous lepidopterist and author F.W. Frohawk, writing in 1934, described the pearl-bordered as one of the commonest of our woodland butterflies just as it was already a declining species in north Essex.

The pearl-bordered fritillary was still to be seen in viable numbers in Friday Wood, Berechurch; Weeleyhall Wood; High Woods, Colchester and a few other North Essex woods until the mid-1950s, but by 1960 it had disappeared with no sign since of recovery. The Friday Wood colony was in a bluebell glade at the lower end of the wood close to the Roman River and Joe Firmin counted more than 20 there in May, 1957. This particular site became scrubbed over with blackthorn bushes and brambles in the early 1960s and the butterfly disappeared, apparently because of habitat deterioration. The same applied to the colony in Weeleyhall Wood, where Ian C. Rose recorded it until the latter years of the 1950s. As well as habitat changes in Essex and Suffolk, the 1950s experienced a succession of cold, wet springs and cool summers which may also have had an effect on the declining populations. An unsuccessful attempt was made to reintroduce the species into a wooded area of the Danbury Ridge, Essex by Essex Wildlife Trust in the early 1990s. Further efforts to bring this attractive species back to woodland in north and mid Essex may be made under the Essex Biodiversity Action Plan but before these are undertaken there will be thorough investigation into the habitat, climatic and life history requirements of a butterfly which obviously suffers from dramatic population swings.

This butterfly has declined in Britain even more alarmingly than has the small pearl-bordered fritillary. There are a few remaining colonies in woods of Surrey, Sussex and Kent, several of them the result of deliberate re-introduction.

(*Jermyn 1827, Raynor 1884, Fitch 1891, Harwood 1903, Firmin 1970, Firmin 1974, Firmin et al. 1975, Corke 1997, Asher et al. 2001*)

HIGH BROWN FRITILLARY (*Argynnis adippe*)

Description:

The upper-side of the male is bright orange-brown marked with black spots and lines and with two lines of black scales on each forewing. On the underside the basal area of the hind-wing has some green shading and the remainder of the wing is marked with silver spots. Towards the margin is a row of silver-pupilled red spots. Females are larger than the males with a more yellowish basal wing colour and lack the forewing black scent scales. Average male wingspan 60mm; female 67mm.

Life History:

The butterfly is on the wing from late June until early August. The yellowish eggs are laid singly usually in leaf litter near the violets, or on the stems or leaves of dog violet (*Viola riviniana*) or other violet species. As the larva inside develops, the egg becomes grey. The larva is visible through the shell, and it remains in this state throughout the winter, hatching in late February and early March. The larvae, when fully grown after the fifth moult, have two distinct colour forms. The dark form is dark brown with a white dorsal stripe and pink spines. The light form has a reddish-brown ground colour with white dorsal stripe and reddish brown spines. The pupa is dark brown with two rows of metallic gold spots. The butterfly hatches after three weeks.

Habitat and Behaviour:

Until the 1950s the high brown fritillary was regarded primarily as a butterfly of woodland clearings and associated with traditional coppicing. But in some regions colonies occurred in wood pasture and on acidic soils and commons where there is plenty of bracken. It is now considered that high brown larvae prefer to bask on bracken in spring to get warm, moving on to violet plants nearby to feed. On warmer days they hide in deeper bracken and in leaf litter. The flight of the butterfly is swift and powerful as it searches for nectar sources such as thistles and bramble blossom.

History:

Jermyn gave Hamlet's and Hartley Woods and Bromley Thickets as Essex localities. Harwood cites Raynor as reporting it 'sparingly' at Hazeleigh and Woodham Mortimer, whilst it was 'common' at Colchester and several of the woods in the North East [of Essex]. The butterfly both lost ground and regained it in several other parts of Essex in the years up to the beginning of the second World War, but it seems that it may have retained its stronghold in the North East Essex woods through this period. There are specimens caught by Blaxill labelled 'Donyland' from 23rd and 30th July 1946 in Colchester Museum collections. The high brown fritillary continued to exist in a number of woods in North Essex and the Colchester area until the late 1950s when, in common with the silver-washed fritillary and the pearl-bordered fritillary, it disappeared from all its favoured sites. The late Donald Blaxill reported it from rides in High Woods, Colchester until the mid-1950s where it flew in sections of the wood which were managed for game and where there were wide rides brushed clear of invasive scrub and where there were tall thistles and other nectar plants. Ian C. Rose regularly saw high browns in the rides and margins of Weeleyhall Wood, Weeley between 1947 and 1956 and Joe Firmin saw up to a dozen each year in June and July in open areas along the southern edge of Donyland Woods between 1952 and 1958. Others were reported during the 1950s from Friday Wood, Berechurch, and from woodland in the Coggeshall area. In view of what is now known about the habitat requirements of this species, it may be relevant, as Corke notes, that the North Essex woods were more open, and interspersed with heath and bracken than is the case today. The high brown is now one of Britain's rarest butterflies confined to only a few localities in the south-west, north west and Wales. Conservation programmes in the butterfly's remaining survival sites in SW and NW England and in Wales, coordinated by Butterfly Conservation, appear to be halting further decline in populations but it is unlikely we will see this fine species back in our local woods in the foreseeable future. Perhaps the most accessible place where this fine butterfly can still be seen is Arnside Knott, Cumbria. It also flies on the fringes of Exmoor and Dartmoor.

(Jermyn 1827, Harwood 1903, Colchester Museum collections, Firmin 1974, Firmin et al. 1975, Corke 1997, Asher et al. 2001).

HEATH FRITILLARY *(Mellicta athalia)* Plate 10

Description:
The upper-side is orange-brown with a lattice of black markings. The under-side of the hind-wing is whitish-yellow with orange bands and black marks. Females are slightly larger and paler, less heavily marked than the males, and with more rounded wings. Wingspan: male 40mm; female 44mm.

Life history:
The butterfly is on the wing in June and July. Females lay eggs on cow-wheat *(Melampyrum pratense)*, in large batches on the underside of the leaves of the foodplant. The eggs are yellowish-white, each with 25 longitudinal keels. They hatch in two weeks. The larva is black, mottled with white and with amber coloured spines. The pupa is white with orange and black marks. It is suspended by tail hooks from a pad of silk attached to a stem or leaf. The larvae, while still young in late August, hibernate until the following March or April among dead, curled up leaves.

Habitat and Behaviour:
This species has two quite distinct habitats, sheltered hollows in heathland in the west country, and open, coppiced woodland in the South East. In this latter habitat (its Essex haunt) it is dependent on an abundance of cow-wheat in recently coppiced or clear-felled areas in woods. This habitat rapidly becomes over-grown and the butterfly requires adjacent areas into which it can move. Unfortunately, it is also very sedentary

in its habits, and so has been very vulnerable to changes in woodland management.

History:
Jermyn gave Hamlet's and Hartley Woods and Bromley Thickets as Essex localities. Until the 1860s it was, according to Harwood, very local but still common in High Woods, Colchester and it was also found in the woods 'bordering the road from Colchester to Ipswich'. However, by the end of the century it was practically confined to those woods. In one of the woods (Birch Wood?) the heath fritillary abounded until about 1890 when, as more cover was needed for game, the underwood was allowed to grow over its whole extent and no fresh clearances were made for several years. The glades were also kept closely clipped and mown which resulted in the total disappearance of all sun-loving plants including the larval foodplants cow-wheat and (as Harwood thought) foxglove. There were no nectar plants such as brambles, thistles and others left for the butterflies. Harwood regretted the lost of the Essex form of *athalia* as this was larger and more richly coloured than any occurring elsewhere. There was also a colony of the heath fritillary in Hartley Wood, Little Clacton until the mid-1800s but this disappeared probably as a result of management changes which eliminated its larval foodplants and also its nectar plants.
The butterfly has been extinct in North East Essex since the early years of the 20th century, but there have been several attempts at re-introducing it to suitably managed woodland elsewhere in the county. It may still be seen at the Essex Wildlife Tust's reserve, Thrift Wood, Bicknacre, and also at Hockley.
(*Jermyn 1827, Fitch 1891, Harwood 1903, Firmin et al. 1975, Corke 1997, Asher et al. 2001*)

GRAYLING (*Hipparchia semele*) Plate 11

Description:
This is a large butterfly (wing span up to 60mm.), which always settles with its wings closed. The under-side hind-wings are finely mottled with greys and browns, with an irregularly wavy thin black line across the middle. The shading tends to be paler in the outer part of the wings, with a variable in ill-defined whitish band in the males. The wing-patterning is more evenly distributed in the females. The underside forewing is orange-brown to yellow, with two well-marked eye-spots on each wing, and a darker greyish border and wing-tip. The upper-sides are a rich dark brown with an orange-brown or yellowish incomplete band towards the outer edges, enclosing two eye-spots on each fore-wing, and usually one more on each of the hind-wings.

Similar Species:
In continental Europe there are many grayling species, several of them virtually indistinguishable from our species. However, in Britain the only species at all likely to be confused with it is the meadow brown, but the more powerful flight of the grayling,

and its quite distinctive underside patterning, make it unmistakable at close quarters.

Life History:
The eggs are white and spherical, generally laid on the grasses which will be eaten by the resulting caterpillars. Several species of grass are used as food-plants, including sheep's fescue (*Festuca ovina*), red fescue (*Festuca rubra*), early hair-grass (*Aira praecox*) and also marram (*Ammophila arenaria*). The caterpillars have longitudinal whitish, brown and yellow stripes, and feed on the grass blades at night. They over-winter in this stage. The chrysalis is formed in a small chamber a few millimetres underground and the adult butterfly emerges around mid-July, continuing to fly through August and into early September.

Habitat and Behaviour:
Dry, well-drained and sunny down-land slopes, heath-land and coastal dunes are the favoured habitats of this species, but it also flourishes in ex-industrial 'brown-field', sites, old quarries and other disturbed sites, where there are areas of bare soil or sand. The males spend long periods of time settled with wings closed, on hot, bare ground or rocks, flying up to inspect passing insects, and intercept females. In cool conditions they angle themselves with wing-surfaces facing the sun, but in hot weather face the sun, thus casting no shadow. Their excellent camouflage makes them difficult to spot, but they fly up when disturbed. The flight is low and powerful, but they usually settle back on the ground a few metres further on. They can sometimes be seen 'mud-puddling', but are less often seen taking nectar from flowers. Areas of disturbed, bare soil or sand, and dry conditions seem to be essential conditions for the grayling, as well, of course, as the presence of the grasses which the larvae feed on. There is a close correlation in North East Essex between the former sites for the grayling butterfly and a very local grasshopper, the mottled grasshopper (*Myrmeliotettix maculatus*), suggesting similar habitat requirements (*Wake 1997*).

History:
Habitat destruction through housing or retail development on heath-land, agricultural intensification, car-park construction on coastal sites, cessation of grazing, and 'improvement' of grass-land elsewhere are among the causes of a national decline of this butterfly. It remains common on some inland heaths, but has become a mainly coastal species in Britain, surviving on coastal dunes and cliff-edges.
In Essex it has always had a very precarious existence, mainly in the North East of the county, but is now believed to be extinct.
Jermyn (1827) gave Lexden Heath as a locality for the grayling, and Fitch added Tiptree Heath, though he thought it already extinct at both localities. Harwood had taken only two or three 'stragglers' in the Colchester area, but several at Birch Wood, Dedham. Harwood himself described it as very rare and local in our area, but speculated that in past times it would have abounded 'on some of the extensive heaths

and moors which surrounded Colchester'. There is evidence of its occurrence near Kelvedon at the beginning of the century, and also reported sightings of single graylings in that area in the late 1940s. It also occurred at West Bergholt, Copford, Birch, Langenhoe and Coggeshall. However, the main former strongholds of the species seem to have been the heathlands to the south of Colchester - notably the heaths around Friday Wood, and further east at Donyland, near Rowhedge. There were also populations at Fingringhoe Wick and Colne Point nature reserves, as reported by Clark and Hobday, following their survey of 1963. Unfortunately there is a gap in the record between Harwood's observations and the 1940s, but some time during this interval the butterfly must have made a significant recovery in the Colchester area. There are museum specimens collected by Blaxill labelled 'Berechurch' and 'Donyland' from 1945, 1946, 1954, and 1957. Huggins, writing in the mid 1950s considered it 'common in several places in the north' [of Essex], notably 'Bere' [presumably Berechurch] common. According to Firmin et al. it was common at several of these sites until the mid 1960s, but became rare both there and at Fingringhoe and Colne Point in the late 1960s.

Seabrook reported a small colony at Weeley in 1949, and Dewick noted its appearance at Bradwell - a singleton in 1948, and several in 1949 and 50. In the same year, Friedlein noted its first appearance at North Fambridge, and saw four at St. Osyth in August. Dewick reported seeing graylings again in 1951, and a female at a new locality. The butterfly still had a 'precarious foot hold' in the district in 1953. Firmin et al. suggest that the late 1940s-early 1950s sightings at N. Fambridge and Bradwell might have been extensions from the North Eastern populations.

The last recorded sighting in the Roman River Valley was 1971, despite extensive searches carried out by Joe Firmin, Ted Benton, Vic Barnham and others. There was then no reliable evidence of the existence of the species in North East Essex until a local resident, Ruth Tucker, reported seeing graylings at buddleia in her garden, in 1982. In 1983 Joe Firmin and Ted Benton searched the nearby Middlewick Range during the grayling's flight period. On 6th August a single male was seen and photographed in a sandy hollow behind the targets at the southern end of the range. The suitable habitat was a small area of dunes and hollows, presumably established by excavation when the raised 'butts' were built. Open, sandy areas with sparse vegetation were interspersed with areas being colonised by bramble and scrub. Evidence of burning and tyre marks suggested that the small area remaining suitable for the graylings had been unintentionally maintained by local youths setting fire to broom and gorse scrub, and by bike scramblers disturbing the sandy soil. Almost immediately after the discovery of the site, the M.o.D. carried out major maintenance work on the habitat, and there were fears that the last remaining colony of the grayling would be wiped out. Difficulties of access due to intensive M.o.D. use of the range limited subsequent monitoring, but visits by Benton on July 27 and Aug 1st 1984 established the continued presence, though in desperately small numbers (4-5 on the second visit), of the species at this site. On 15th Aug. 1986 a one-hour search of the Middlewick site revealed just four graylings, one male and three females, two of the latter on recently excavated sand (Ted Benton).

Goodey carried out twelve transects of the site between 10th July and 1st Sept. 1987. The most individuals seen on any one occasion was three, on Aug. 4th, underlining how precarious was the hold of the species at its last known North East Essex site. Goodey attributed the drastic decline of the species since the late 1960s to a combination of factors, including the loss of rabbit-grazing due to myxomatosis, the isolation of small colonies, poor weather for a series of summers, and reduced drainage of soils, affecting the survival of the subterranean pupae. Goodey and Firmin summarised the decline of the species at its Middlewick site from eight seen in each of 1987 and 1988, to two in 1989, none in 1990, and one in 1991 - the last known sighting at this locality. Occasional 'stragglers' have been seen since, notably one in a garden at Great Oakley basking briefly on a wooden post on 10th August 1995 (Jerry Bowdrey, pers. comm.). *(Jermyn 1827, Fitch 1891, Harwood 1903, Colchester Museum collections, Huggins 1956, Williams, Essex Naturalist 28, p.210, Seabrook, Essex Naturalist 28, p.211, Dewick 1951, Friedlein 1951, Dewick 1956a, 1956b, Clark & Hobday 1966, Firmin et al. 1975, Firmin 1978c, Benton 1983, 1984, Goodey 1987, Goodey & Firmin 1992)*

THE COLOUR PLATES

In the plates, the following abbreviations and symbols are used:

ups   upper-side of wings

uns   under-side of wings

♂   male of species

♀   female of species

See the descriptions for the sizes of butterflies.

Small skipper ♂
Page 10

Small skipper ♀

Small skipper, uns

Small skipper
Note antennae

Essex skipper ♂
Page 11

Essex skipper
Note black tipped antennae

Plate 1

Essex skipper ♀

Large skipper ♂
Page 13

Large skipper ♀

Large skipper, uns

Dingy skipper ♀
Page 57

Grizzled skipper ♀
Page 58

Plate 2

Clouded yellow ♂ uns
Page 49

Brimstone ♂ uns
Page 14

Brimstone ♀ uns

Brimstone
Newly emerged, with pupa case

Large white ♂ ups
Page 15

Large white ♀ ups

Plate 3

Small white ♂
Spring generation
Page 16

Small white ♀
Summer generation

Small white ♀ uns
Summer generation

Green-veined white ♂
Summer generation
Plate 18

Green-veined white ♀
Spring generation

Green-veined white ♂ uns
Spring generation

Plate 4

Orange tip ♂ ups
Page 19

Orange tip ♀ uns & ups

Orange tip ♂ uns

Green hairstreak, uns
Page 20

Purple hairstreak ♂ ups
Page 22

Purple hairstreak ♀ ups

Plate 5

Purple hairstreak ♀ uns

White-letter hairstreak, uns
Page 24

Small copper, ups
Page 26

Small copper, uns

Brown argus ♂ ups
Page 28

Brown argus ♀ ups

Plate 6

Brown argus, uns

Common blue ♂ ups
Page 30

Common blue, typical ♀ ups

Common blue, blue ♀ ups

Common blue uns

Holly blue ♂ ups
Page 32

Plate 7

Holly blue ♀ ups

Holly blue, uns

White admiral, ups
Page 33

White admiral, uns

Purple emperor ♂ ups
Page 63

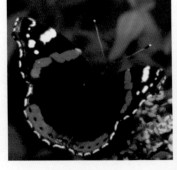

Red admiral, ups
Page 55

Plate 8

Painted lady, ups
Page 54

Small tortoiseshell, ups
Page 35

Camberwell beauty, ups
Page 52

Peacock, ups
Page 36

Comma, ups
Page 37

Comma, uns

Plate 9

Silver-washed fritillary ♂ ups
Page 39

Silver-washed fritillary ♀ ups

Silver-washed fritillary, uns

Heath fritillary, ups
Page 72

Speckled wood ♂ ups
Page 41

Speckled wood ♀ ups

Plate 10

Wall ♂ ups
Page 42

Wall ♀ ups

Marbled white, ups
Page 43

Grayling, uns
Page 73

Gatekeeper ♂ ups
Page 44

Gatekeeper ♀ ups

Plate 11

Meadow brown ♂ ups
Page 45

Meadow brown ♀ ups

Meadow brown ♀ uns

Ringlet, ups
Page 46

Pair of ringlets, uns

Small heath, uns
Page 47

Plate 12

Chapter 5   WHERE TO WATCH BUTTERFLIES

Butterfly Distribution

Anyone who has compared the range of species illustrated in the standard field-guides with those that can be seen in their neighbourhood will be well aware that butterflies are not evenly distributed round the country. The more committed observers soon find that they have to travel quite large distances to see the more localised 'target' species. So what influences the presence or absence of a species in any particular neighbourhood? The main influences can be grouped into three main categories: range, habitat and history. The range of a butterfly is the large scale geographical area within which it can be found, given other factors are suitable. The range of a butterfly's distribution is mainly the resultant of the past formation of geological barriers such as mountain ranges and oceans together with the climatic limits within which it can survive. However, many species occur only very locally even within their geographical range. This is because they may have specialised habitat requirements. Most obviously, they will be dependent on sufficient quantities of the caterpillar's food-plant. So, for example, butterflies such as the Adonis blue and chalk-hill blue only occur on chalk or limestone downland where their caterpillars' food-plant, horseshoe vetch (*Hippocrepis comosa*) grows. Even there, loss of grazing by sheep or rabbits can lead to rank grasses and scrub development shading out the vetches with subsequent decline and local extinction of the butterflies. In North East Essex we lack the chalk or chalky boulder clay of the West of the county, so we do not have, and probably never have had, resident populations of these chalk downland species. So, botany and geology are of crucial importance if we are to predict which species to expect in an area. Other factors will also be significant, of course. Some British species are at the northern limit of their geographical range, and will survive only in the most favourable habitats, often very much more specialised ones than nearer to the centre of their range. Local populations of such species are usually more vulnerable to local extinctions due to alterations in their habitats, adverse changes in climate and so on. Perhaps of greater significance than any of these other aspects of habitat is the fact that virtually all the environments in which butterflies now exist are the result of human activity (or neglect). Many of our most familiar species have co-evolved alongside long-run traditional methods of land-management, whether coppicing and ride-maintenance in woodlands, grazing of meadows and heaths, cutting of hay meadows and so on. The transformation of the countryside since the second world war by grant-subsidised industrial agriculture has changed these traditionally maintained habitats beyond recognition. Such butterflies as survive do so on the margins of the new agricultural monocultures, in remaining hedgerows, roadside verges, the few remaining patches of 'waste ground' and in nature reserves or amenity land of various sorts. It is now increasingly recognised that urban and suburban parks, gardens, allotment sites and ex-industrial 'brown-field' sites provide vital habitat resources for species increasingly unable to survive in the intensively farmed countryside.

Until relatively recently the efforts of conservationists were concentrated on buying and managing small nature reserves, and seeking to protect important sites from adverse changes through designation as Sites of Special Scientific Interest. Increasingly, however, it has become clear that preserving these small oases of wild-life diversity in the midst of the intensively farmed 'desert' was insufficient. Small, isolated populations were often too genetically uniform, and vulnerable to local extinction. Of course, in the past, such local extinctions always took place, but species would be able to recolonise from nearby populations as conditions became suitable again. The distances between tiny, isolated pockets of suitable habitat are now so great that recolonisation is often not possible. This is why the history of a site is so important: a locality may appear to be entirely suitable for a species which is nevertheless absent because of some past event, such as a fire, pesticide spraying or ploughing, but the species has no nearby population to spread back into it. The emphasis now has to be on protecting and improving the management of urban open spaces in favour of butterflies and other wildlife, whilst at the same time working for radical changes in agricultural practices in the wider countryside. There is growing evidence that less intensive, more wild life-friendly agricultural systems can be at least as productive, and less costly both in environmental and financial terms.

North East Essex Then and Now

North East Essex was, in the 19th century, one of the richest butterfly haunts in Britain. Though it lacked the species associated with chalk downland, it had an abundance of large deciduous woodlands, heaths and meadows. We are exceptionally well-informed about the past wealth of butterflies in the area because of the records and collections made by many eminent local naturalists: John Ray, late 17th c., L. Jermyn, early 19th, then Dr Maclean of Colchester, Rev. G. H. Raynor of Maldon, E. Doubleday, G. F. Mathew, of Dovercourt and W. H. Harwood who studied and collected in the Colchester district in the latter part of the century (see chapter 6). Even then there were expressions of dismay at the loss of habitat, and adverse changes in woodland management, but the presence of such woodland species as the heath, pearl-bordered, small pearl-bordered, high brown and silver-washed fritillaries, purple emperor, white admiral, large tortoiseshell, Duke of Burgundy, and wood white, some of them even listed as common and widespread in those days, makes depressing reading today. Favoured localities mentioned over and again included: the larger woods around Colchester (High Woods and Donyland particularly often named), the woods either side of the road from Colchester to Ipswich (Dedham, Birch and Langham Hall Wood), Lexden Heath, Bromley Thicks, Mundon Furz and Hazeleigh (Maldon), Riddles Wood, Maldon Wood and Hartley Wood (between St. Osyth and Weeley), Little (now Copperas) and Great Stour Woods (Ramsey and Wrabness) and Coggeshall (presumably Honey wood and the woods of Markshall). Some classic localities, such as Bromley Thicks, a favourite haunt of Laetitia Jermyn, had been entirely destroyed before Harwood's time. The 'Thicks' covered a very large area between Little Bentley and Elmsted Market, and the Chapman & André map (based on a survey of 1773-4) indicates a combination of wood and heathland. It must have been a delight to visit, with wood white, pearl-bordered and small pearl-bordered fritillaries, Duke of Burgundy, high brown, dark green and silver-washed fritillaries, and many more. Also destroyed early on was Lexden Heath, one of Jermyn's localities for the grayling. Chapman & André show this as a large area between Lexden, Shrub End and Stanway, but by the first Ordnance Survey maps, based on a survey 1874/6, it was largely enclosed for agriculture, with only a narrow strip of remaining heath. Harwood regarded the grayling as rare, but commented: 'Probably it abounded on some of the extensive heaths and moors that surrounded Colchester in past times.' (1903, p. 141). Others of these favourite haunts of the early butterfly-hunters were partially cleared and fragmented, and subjected to changes in woodland management. Comparison of Chapman & André's survey with that of the O.S. a century later shows that much of the loss of woodland in North East Essex took place during that period, with surprisingly little since. Figs. 3a, b and c show the three areas of woodland north of St. Osyth which were favourite haunts of Jermyn and the other early lepidopterists: Maldon, Riddles and Hartley Woods. All three are based on the current 1998 O.S. survey, showing changes in woodland cover in relation to current features. The first gives approximate extents of the three woods as shown by Chapman & André, the second the same woods as they were in the 1870s (and as Harwood would have known them), and the third shows their current extent. Chapman & André show Maldon Wood as a large unbroken expanse, with areas of heathland adjacent to it and linking it with both Hartley and Riddles Woods. By the 1870s a large section of Hartley Wood had been cleared, dividing it into two separate woodland patches. Heathland had been enclosed for agriculture or building, Maldon Wood had been reduced by more then half, and the smaller area of woodland formerly lying between Maldon and Hartley woods had been reduced to a tiny fragment. In connection with the status of several of the woodland butterflies, Harwood commented on the loss of woodland, and how fragmentation would prevent recolonisation of woods after local extinctions. Between the 1870s and the most recent O. S. survey, Maldon Wood has been further reduced to two fragments of its former self, and the northern section of Hartley Wood has disappeared. However, both Riddles and the remainder of Hartley Woods retain their old boundaries. Similarly with other favourite haunts of the 19th century butterfly-hunters. High Woods, Colchester, Weeley Wood, and Stour Wood, Wrabness retain their old boundaries. Clearly, the loss of our woodland species cannot be explained entirely by the loss of woodland. Other factors, include changes in woodland management - either neglect or replanting with conifers - fragmentation of remaining extensive woodland, and agricultural intensification around woodland edges and between woods need to be considered.

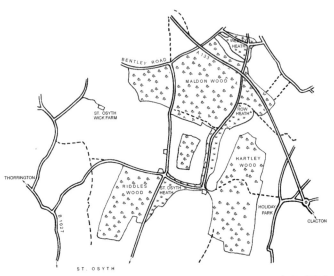

Fig.3a: Derived from the Chapman & André, Survey 1773-4, Published 1777
and the Ordnance Survey , 1998

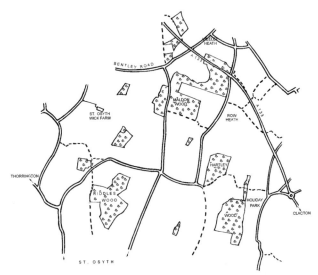

Fig. 3b: Derived from the First Ordnance Survey, 1874-6, Published 1880
and the Ordnance Survey , 1998

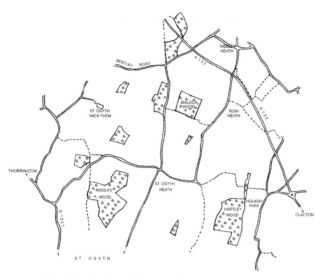

Fig. 3c: Derived from Ordnance Survey, 1998

The following account, by Ian Rose, of the changes in and around Weeley Wood, another classic locality, illustrates the impact of these changes in our local countryside.

Weeley Woods - a butterfly paradise lost

The large tract of woodland at Weeley, in the heart of the Tendring Hundred, known as Weeley Woods, was a haven for wildlife before and during the second world war and into the 1950s. Owned by Roger Weeley, son of Squire Weeley, the woods were in the hands of an ardent nature lover and conservationist who could never be accused of 'prairie farming'. Small fields abounded, hedges were wide and untrimmed providing nesting sites and food for a variety of birds and animals.

Today the surviving remnant of the original ancient woodland, known as Weeleyhall Wood, covers 78 acres (*31 hectares*) and is an Essex Wildlife Trust reserve.

When the wood was owned by the Weeley family it was surrounded by open scrubby heathland which sloped up to the trees at the wood edges. The entrance on the north side was at the lowest part and very wet and marshy, increasing the biodiversity of the area with sallow trees and giant marsh thistles.

The wood had not been gamekeepered during the second world war and it was a joy to see fox cubs playing in the hay fields, leaping over the bales. When vermin control was resumed in the post war period, 57 feral cats were removed from the wood in the first year. This had a positive effect on the wildlife population. Small birds and mammals were able to regain their territories. Inside the wood the rides were wide and clear, allowing the sun to reach the tracks edged by brambles, nettles and low shrubs which

93

tapered up to the tree canopy of mainly sweet chestnut, oak and birch. During the summer months high brown and silver-washed fritillary butterflies nectared on the abundant flowers of marsh thistles, while white admirals glided throughout the wood seeking the bramble blossoms. The thriving tangles of honeysuckle provided food for the larvae of the white admirals which feed on the plant's leaves. Larvae of the two large species of fritillaries feed on the leaves of violet and there were plenty of these plants in the wood. Outside the wood, on the heath, pearl-bordered fritillaries flourished, as did meadow browns, small heaths, wall brown and green hairstreak butterflies. Purple and white-letter hairstreaks enjoyed the wood edges - plenty of oak leaves for the larvae of the purple hairstreaks and elm and wych elm leaves for the white-letter hairstreaks. Up until the mid-1950s large tortoiseshells could be seen along the wood margins, but along with the fritillaries this beautiful species disappeared from the area by the late 1950s.

Adders basked in the sun on the heath and in the open rides during the day, while at night glow worms lit the ride verges. MV lamps and generators were not available in those days, but a torch and net at dusk would produce a very good selection of moths and a little sugaring (a mixture smeared on trees and bushes) would top up the list. The wood was alive with bird song. Nightingales and warblers nested and most species of titmice occurred without the aid of nest boxes. Finches and yellowhammers nested in the scrub and brambles on the heath and even pairs of red-backed shrikes could be found along the hedgerows. Sadly the wood today is a shadow of its former wildlife glory despite the commendable management efforts of the Wildlife Trust. The farm is a one-field prairie monoculture, the heath has gone, there are no hedges and the plough goes right up to the boundary of the wood which is isolated as the linking hedges have gone and the important edge vegetation is missing. The great butterfly days of the old wildwood are just a fading memory. Progress?

Where to Watch Butterflies Today
However, there are reasons to be optimistic. Some woods, such as Stour and Copperas Woods, Wrabness, Friday Wood, Colchester, and the woods to the north of Coggeshall retain much of their entomological richness, and are now being managed to the benefit of their butterfly populations. Other woods, such as Colchester's High Woods remain relatively less well endowed with butterflies despite now being well managed as part of the country park, though more species may well colonise in the future. A very promising development is the change in policy of the government forestry agency, Forest Enterprise, which has now turned away from its previously very adverse practice of dense conifer plantation. Woods such as Chalkney, near Earls Colne, parts of the Markshall complex north of Coggeshall and Broakes Wood, Halstead are already benefiting greatly from the new regime.

Although the expansion of arable farming in the Colchester area and North East Essex, and forestry changes in the two decades after the Second World War robbed many butterfly species of vital habitats and pockets of survival, there remain plenty of places where you can watch, study and photograph butterflies. Some woods are now being better managed with regard to wildlife and some farmers and landowners are bearing in mind the need for conservation in their production programmes. The Environment Agency is also aware of the importance of sea walls as sanctuaries for a surprising number of butterfly and moth species and, in consultation with English Nature and wildlife conservation organisations, has undertaken a more careful and sensitive programme of vegetation mowing and protective work projects in recent years.

WOODLANDS

Friday Wood, Berechurch

Friday Wood covers 225 acres (*90 ha*) in the Roman River Conservation Zone and remains one of the best sites close to Colchester to see a good variety of woodland and grass/heath butterfly species. Sadly, like many other area woods, it has lost its colonies of the silver-washed fritillary, pearl-bordered fritillary, and large tortoiseshell, while the grayling, which was once reasonably common on heathland and sandy grassland adjoining the wood, had also disappeared by the 1960s. Also lost in the 1980s were the grizzled skipper and the dingy skipper which were also found in the heathland and scrubland surrounding the main woodland area. But a walk in the wood's rides, or along the margins beside the river, in spring and summer will be rewarded by sightings of orange tip, green-veined white, holly blue, speckled wood (newly emerged in April and May) and hibernated small tortoiseshells, commas and peacocks, with the occasional brimstone. Common blues and brown argus are in the heathy and grassy areas in June (with second broods in August) followed by many meadow browns, ringlets and gatekeepers in July and August. Also frequent in the open grass and heath areas are small copper, small heath, large skipper, small skipper and Essex skipper. The white-letter hairstreak, the caterpillars of which feed on the blossoms and leaves of elm and wych elm, has suffered losses from the spread of Dutch elm disease, but there are still scattered colonies in the Friday Wood and Roman River Valley area. Look for the butterflies in July nectaring on bramble blooms and thistle blooms. The purple hairstreak is still common on the oaks of Friday Wood, its larvae feeding on the bracts and leaves, but the green hairstreak, while still to be found where broom and gorse bushes grow on the heaths and wood margins, is less common than in the 1950s and 1960s. The graceful white admiral disappeared from Friday Wood and all other woods in North East Essex apart from Stour Wood, Wrabness, in the late 1950s but there was excitement in 1995 when Dr. Chris Gibson of English Nature, during an invertebrate survey in Friday Wood discovered some white admirals in a part of the wood where they were present until the 1960s fade-out. Since then the white admiral has been seen in Friday Wood in July and early August in small numbers which would appear to indicate either a recolonisation or perhaps an un-notified release.

Friday Wood is an ancient woodland owned by the Ministry of Defence and is still used for training purposes. On a visit you should keep to the waymarked rights of way and obey the Army warning notices. The main parking area is on the minor road which runs south from Berechurch Hall Road to Layer-de-la Haye parallel to the B1026. The area can be accessed by the 67 bus service from Colchester town centre in the direction of West Mersea, alighting at the Cherry Tree, Blackheath, or by service 8, alighting on Berechurch Hall road, and taking a metalled lane by M. o. D. establishments. The site is accessible at all times.

Also worth a visit for a butterfly walk is the **Roman River Valley** nature reserve managed by Essex Wildlife Trust. The Roman River is a narrow stream at this point and wanders through marsh and woodland. The woodland is part of Needle Eye Wood where you can see some of the butterfly species found in Friday Wood. Entrance is on the west side of the B1026 (Colchester-Layer) just north of Kingsford Bridge. Bus service 50, from Colchester to Tollesbury, passes the reserve entrance. Alternatively, a longer walk along the Roman River, taking in the reserve, can be started at Heckford Bridge (Colchester to Maldon bus service 75) or from Friday Wood. The reserve is accessible at all times.

Markshall Estate, Coggeshall

The Markshall Estate covers some 2,000 acres including large areas of ancient woodland. There are also extensive areas of grassland supporting butterfly species. More than 150 acres of the estate are enclosed and hold an arboretum and formal gardens and a further 300 acres are accessible by waymarked footpaths. The estate was left to the nation by its last owner, Thomas Phillips Price and is managed by the Thomas Phillips Price Trust which is engaged in a major programme of restoration. The estate is a major reserve for woodland and grassland butterflies and has been selected under the Essex Biodiversity Action Plan for the reintroduction of a group of woodland butterflies, most of which were found in the past in the estate woods. The first of these reintroductions is of the silver-washed fritillary, a beautiful, large tawny-brown species which was found at Markshall until the 1960s but died out, as in other area woods. Female silver-washed fritillaries obtained from donor colonies in Surrey were released in July, 1999 with reinforcement stock in 2000 and 2001 resulting in an encouraging number of offspring being seen in the summers of 2000 and 2001. It is hoped that other 'lost' woodland species will be brought back to the Markshall woods in the next decade.

The purple hairstreak is widespread on the oaks in the estate woods and there are one or two colonies of the white-letter hairstreak on surviving elms. The speckled wood is common in two broods throughout the woodland complex and the grassy areas support large numbers of the meadow brown, ringlet, gatekeeper, small heath, large skipper, small skipper, Essex skipper, common blue and small copper. In spring there are many orange tips to be seen where their larval foodplant, the cuckoo flower (lady's smock) grows in damp grassland. The green-veined white is also common in two broods. The holly blue is also reasonably common in spring and late summer broods in most years.

By car the estate is reached via a turning off the B1024 to Earls Colne north of Coggeshall. Follow the large brown and white signs from the A120. Pay and display car park. By public transport the regular service 70 between Colchester and Braintree will take you to Coggeshall. There are two excellent cafes for refreshment stops, prior to a pleasant walk by footpaths to Markshall. A left turn in the village leads across the by-pass and by Bungate and Monks Wood, or north along the main street leads to a footpath across fields and on to the access lane for Markshall. The visitor centre in a 15th century barn is open from Easter until October 31st except non-Bank Holiday Mondays, 10.30am to 4.30pm on weekdays and to 5pm on weekends and Bank Holidays. Waymarked walks start from the Centre.

Broaks Wood, Gosfield

This 155 acre (*62 ha*) wood, much of it of ancient origin, is managed for the Forestry Commission by Forest Enterprise. There are many open rides and glades which support a good range of butterfly and moth species. In spring it is a good site to see brimstone butterflies just out of hibernation as well as freshly-emerged orange tips, green-veined whites and speckled woods. Common blues, brown argus and small coppers can be seen in the flowery open areas and there are also flourishing colonies of meadow browns, gatekeepers and ringlets. Purple hairstreaks are widespread on the oaks and the green hairstreak has also been recorded where there are broom bushes. There are also good numbers of skipper butterflies in the grassy rides as well as peacock, small tortoiseshell and comma nectaring on the bramble blossom and thistle blooms in the summer.
The main entrance is on the Hedingham Road (A1017 Braintree-Hedingham) two miles west of Halstead. The 352 bus service between Chelmsford, Braintree and Halstead passes close by the wood. Alternatively there are two pleasant footpath walks from Halstead to the wood (88 service from Colchester to Halstead). The wood is accessible at all times. A 3km waymarked nature trail (red posts) takes in most of the most interesting butterfly sites.

Stour Estuary Nature Reserve, Wrabness

The RSPB Stour Estuary Nature Reserve covers 447 hectares of which 62 ha (155 acres) is classified as semi-natural broad-leaved coppice with standards, dominated by sweet chestnut but with an underlying mixture of native species including small-leaved lime and wild service tree clones. The woodland areas (known as Stour Wood) are broken up by an extensive maintained ride system and there are a number of small ponds. The remaining areas of the reserve consist of intertidal mud flats and salt marsh. The Woodland Trust owns Stour Wood and leases it to the Royal Society for the Protection of Birds.
Stour Wood supports 22 species of butterflies of which the white admiral is the most notable. The wood is the only long-term viable site in Essex for this elegant species. It

is often seen near the reserve car park gliding gracefully around the tops of trees or feeding on bramble blossoms in July.

A fixed transect has been recorded annually since 1983 as part of the national Butterfly Monitoring Scheme operated under the auspices of the Institute of Terrestrial Ecology.

By car, Stour Wood is reached by turning off the A120 Colchester-Harwich road on to the B1352. The main entrance with car park is sign posted from the road. The wood is close to Wrabness rail station, with regular connections to Harwich, Ipswich and Colchester.

Copperas Wood

Copperas Wood, like Stour Wood, is an SSSI, is owned by Essex Wildlife Trust and is reached down a footpath (the route to the Essex Way) beside a large white flat-roofed house. There is parking for one or two cars on the verge. Copperas Wood, like Stour Wood, is good for a range of woodland and grass area butterflies and 23 species have been recorded. As in Stour Wood purple hairstreaks are notable in July and August.

Chalkney Wood, Earls Colne

Chalkney Wood has both great historical and wildlife interest and contains the largest concentration of small-leaved lime trees in Essex. It is one of the finest tracts of ancient woodland left in the county. The south-west part of the 200 acre(80ha) wood is owned by Essex County Council and managed as a public open space. The remainder, running down to the River Colne, is owned by the Forestry Commission which planted much of it with conifers. As these are harvested, original native trees are being allowed to grow through and regenerate. As a result of its long history of coppicing Chalkney Wood has a rich ground flora and supports a good range of woodland and open glade butterflies. In spring there are plenty of orange tips, green-veined whites, first brood speckled woods and hibernated brimstones and in summer the open grassy areas are full of meadow browns, gatekeepers with some ringlets. There are purple hairstreaks on the oaks and where there are flowering thistles peacocks, small tortoiseshells and commas are regular feeders on the blooms.

The main entrance to the wood is a mile down a minor road leaving the A1124 (Colchester-Halstead - bus service 88) between Earls Colne and White Colne. It can also be entered from the north via a footpath running south from the A1124 at White Colne to Chalkney Mill. It is accessible at all times.

High Woods Country Park, Colchester

This patchwork of woods, meadows, marsh and grassy rough ground was bought by Colchester Borough Council in 1979 to save it from the residential development which now surrounds it. The woods in the stream valley to the north, known as the Central

Valley, are a remnant of the once Royal Forest of Kingswood. The mosaic of trees, scrub and open, flowery grassland in the eastern section of the Country Park, which covers a total of 330 acres (*132ha*) is home to a rich variety of invertebrates. The butterflies here are meadow brown, gatekeeper, small heath, common blue, brown argus, small copper, large skipper, small skipper and Essex skipper. Purple hairstreaks are found on the oaks throughout the wood and there is a growing population of speckled woods which are expanding their range throughout East Essex. In spring there are orange tips and green-veined whites and there is usually a good summer showing of the Vanessid butterflies, peacock, small tortoiseshell and comma. Usually the holly blue is present in the spring and summer broods.

The main entrance to the park is off Turner Road which leaves the A134 Colchester-Sudbury road north of Colchester North Station. Car parks are open from 7am to 10pm in summer and the visitor centre is open daily from April to September inclusive. The Country Park is also accessible via its 'southern slopes'. These can easily be reached by a short walk from the town centre, crossing the by-pass near the Leisure centre, and using public footpaths under the railway line.

SEA WALLS AND COASTAL GRASSLAND

Cudmore Grove Country Park, East Mersea

This Essex County Council park is managed by the council's ranger service and covers 35 acres(*14ha*). It has flower-rich grassland and can boast a total of 25 butterfly species with no fewer than 17 being recorded in one day alone in August, 1996. Meadow brown, gatekeeper and small heath are all common residents in summer (June/July). Also common are the small skipper, Essex skipper and large skipper in the meadow and grassland areas. The common blue is present in good numbers and the brown argus is a recent colonist since being first seen in 1996. The small copper is resident with a fluctuating population in two broods. The speckled wood is a recent colonist, first seen in 1992, and the wall brown has a small resident population. Green hairstreaks have been located in the park in 1997 (2 in May); 2 in May, 1999. The purple hairstreak is considered a rare vagrant. In spring orange tips and green veined whites are regularly seen and maintain a small population. The sea wall flowers and vegetation along the stretch towards the Strood, West Mersea also attract a large population of meadow browns, gatekeepers and common blues with some colonies of the brown argus. The small tortoiseshell and peacock are common residents while the red admiral and painted lady are regular immigrants and summer residents. The comma has a small resident population. When there is a sizable immigration of clouded yellows, as in 2001, Cudmore Grove is a good site for this dashing and beautiful visitor from southern Europe.

The country park is open from 8am until dusk all year round. By car, it is reached by bearing left to East Mersea after crossing the Strood causeway at West Mersea (B1025) from Colchester. The country park is beyond East Mersea village, off Bromans Lane and is well sign posted. Access by public transport is not convenient. Bus service 67 from Colchester terminates at West Mersea. From there it is a substantial walk along the south coast of the island, or a taxi journey to the country park.

Copt Hall, Little Wigborough

This is a working farm to the north of the Salcott Channel and owned by the National Trust. The Trust encourages its tenant farmers to farm in a wildlife friendly way and there are headlands with vegetation attractive to invertebrates and well-managed hedgerows. The 400 acre (*160ha*) area contains large populations of butterflies associated with grassland and hedge margins, especially meadow brown, gatekeeper, small heath, large skipper, small skipper, Essex skipper, common blue, green hairstreak and brown argus. The green hairstreak was discovered along one of the hedges in 2002. The sea wall flowers and vegetation also support lots of butterflies and moths and the small copper is commonly found there in two broods where its larval foodplant, sheep's sorrel, flourishes. Peacocks and small tortoiseshells are common, enjoying the nectar provided by thistles and bramble blossom next to the dykes.

The site is reached south of the minor road which joins the B1026 to the B1025 south of Abberton Reservoir via Peldon. Turn off into Copt Hall Lane (signed) and follow signs to National Trust car park at Lower Barn. It is accessible at all times. Access by public transport is difficult. Services 50 and 92 from Colchester stop at Great Wigborough, and 67A, D and E (Colchester to West Mersea) go via Peldon. From either of these to Copt Hall is an unpleasant walk by road.

HEATHS AND ASSOCIATED OPEN AREAS

Hilly Fields, Colchester

This is an important wildlife habitat covering 40 acres (*16ha*). Together with the neighbouring Cymbeline Meadows the area forms part of a ribbon of green open spaces which run from the west of the town, through the heart of the town via the Castle Park and out on the eastern side. Managed by Colchester Borough Council as a public open space, Hilly Fields is a diverse mosaic of habitats supporting a surprising variety of invertebrates, especially butterflies and moths. Much of it is scrub grassland which developed after farming ceased 40 years ago. The low-lying north west area is an interesting example of emerging oak woodland where in July you may see purple hairstreaks. The flat open area of grassland close to the Sussex Road entrance has good colonies of meadow brown, gatekeeper and small heath. The eastern end of the site towards the town is an interesting example of heath left over from a much larger heathland which existed before Colchester spread out. Common blue, brown argus and small copper can be seen in this section as well as all three species of skipper associated with grassy areas. Green hairstreak can also be seen around broom and gorse bushes in May. At the foot of higher ground close to Cymbeline Way lies an area of spring-fed marsh and in the marginal vegetation here in spring you can see orange tip and green-veined white. Also recorded from Hilly Fields are wall brown, speckled wood and holly blue, while on bramble blossom and thistle flowers in summer peacock, small tortoiseshell and comma are regularly seen. Hilly Fields can be reached from Sussex Road (off Lexden Road). Footpaths lead to it from Elianore Road, Sheepen Road, Balkerne Hill and Popes Lane.

Buntings Meadow (25 acres) to the west of Hilly Fields has a butterfly trail which is good for all the usual grassland species as well as common blue, peacock, small tortoiseshell and comma. Purple hairstreak breeds on oaks fringing the site. It can be accessed on foot from Hilly Fields.

Tiptree Heath

This is a small fragment of a large heath which used to stretch from Maldon to Messing. It is the finest and largest surviving heath in Essex covering 60 acres and the only place you will find all three heather species growing together. It has been designated a Site of Special Scientific Interest (SSSI) and is managed by Tiptree Parish Council supported by local conservation groups including CNHS. Encroaching birch and oak scrub continues to be a management problem but special efforts are made to restore the heather and associated flora. The heath is home to a good population of meadow brown, gatekeeper, small heath, common blue, brown argus, large, small and Essex skippers, small copper, and holly blue. Purple hairstreak and green hairstreak are regularly seen and in spring orange tip, green-veined white and brimstone. The heath straddles the B1022 (Colchester-Maldon) on the Maldon side of Tiptree. There is a regular bus service passing (75, between Colchester and Maldon) and car parking beside the heath, which is accessible at all times.

Fordham Heath

This is a surviving remnant of ancient wet heathland managed by Eight Ash Green Parish Council with assistance from the River Colne Countryside Project. The heath was grazed by Commoners' cattle until the Second World War but when this ceased there was invasion by birch, oak, blackthorn and aspen. Much of the heather and gorse disappeared but current management is aimed at scrub control and restoration of heather heath and open flowery grassland. It is an area of 36 acres, good for meadow brown, gatekeeper, small heath, skippers(three species), common blue and brown argus. In the wooded area purple hairstreak is regularly seen as well as holly blue. Brambles and tall thistles attract peacock, small tortoiseshell and comma and in spring you can see orange tip and green-veined white in the damp grassland areas. Brimstones are usually sighted after hibernation.

By car, turn north off the 41124 Colchester-Halstead road in Eight Ash Green, about 800 metres north of its junction with the A12. Car parking opposite the Cricketers public house and next to the road leading to Fordham. Bus service 88 between Colchester and Halstead passes close to the heath at Eight Ash Green. Alternatively there are pleasant walks to it from West Bergholt via Cook's Mill, or Stanway or Lexden via Halstead road and the track which crosses the main railway line at TL954256 (passing EWT reserve Iron Latch meadow). The Heath is accessible at all times.

Fingringhoe Wick Nature Reserve
Although mainly thought of as a prime estuary site created from old gravel workings by Essex Wildlife Trust into its premier sanctuary, this 125 acre (*50ha*) reserve has a significant area of gorse and broom heathland which supports one of the best colonies of the green hairstreak in North East Essex. The grassy areas abound with meadow brown, gatekeeper, small heath, common blue, brown argus, small skipper, Essex skipper, and large skipper. Speckled wood, which is spreading in North East Essex, is present as well as small numbers of wall brown which has become scarcer over the past decade. Purple hairstreaks are on the oaks and holly blue is found in both broods. Spring brings orange tip, green-veined and small white and there's usually a good showing of two broods of the small copper.
The reserve is three miles south east of Colchester, sign posted from there with brown Nature Reserve signs. Take the B1025 from Colchester towards Mersea. After crossing the Roman River turn first left and follow signs. There is a limited bus service between Colchester and Fingringhoe (66A, 66C and 76C). However, there is a more regular service between Colchester and Rowhedge (66), from where there is a pleasant footpath walk to Fingringhoe. The reserve is approximately 1.5 miles further by quiet lane or footpath. The Visitor Centre is open daily except Mondays from 9am to 5pm and the reserve from 9am to 7pm in summer. Visitors to the reserve must go to the Centre to obtain a day permit.

Great Holland Pits, Great Holland
This Essex Wildlife Trust reserve of 40 acres (*16 ha*) is on the site of former gravel workings. Habitats include heathy grassland, pasture, a remnant of old woodland, large and small pools and some wet depressions. It has a wide variety of flowering plants which support healthy colonies of butterflies and moths. During spring and summer butterfly species which may be seen in the reserve are large white, small white, green-veined white, orange tip, green hairstreak, purple hairstreak, small copper, holly blue, common blue, brown argus, red admiral, peacock, painted lady, small tortoiseshell, comma, speckled wood, wall brown, meadow brown, gatekeeper, small heath, small skipper, Essex skipper, and large skipper. In good migration years clouded yellows may also be seen.

The reserve entrance is 800 yards west of the Lion's Den public house, Great Holland, north of the Little Clacton Road. Buses stop at the Lion's Den on the route from Clacton to Walton. The reserve is accessible at all times. For information call the warden on 01255 436494.

Other coastal sites include **Holland Haven Country Park**, and the sea wall to the west of **Jaywick**. These have a good range of common grassland species, including small numbers of the wall brown butterfly. They are also good places to visit for the occasional lucky sighting of the migratory clouded yellow or painted lady. Holland Haven can be reached from Frinton or Clacton by walking along the sea wall. Jaywick can be reached from Clacton by bus services 10 or 11. For further ideas about where to look consult Tony Gunton's excellent *Wild Essex* (2000), which covers the above sites and many more in our area.

Chapter 6   BUTTERFLY HUNTERS

In the 18th, 19th and 20th centuries the Colchester area had a number of regionally and nationally-notable entomologists and field naturalists whose studies of butterfly life histories and records of sightings and captures were of great value and in some instances the first to be described and published. The earliest significant scientific recorder of butterflies was the famous **John Ray** of Black Notley, the 'father' of British natural history. Ray began collecting insects in 1690 and by that time he had already published several works on natural history. He carefully described butterflies and moths found near his home or sent to him by friends. He had a set of chip boxes and breeding cages and his specimens were kept, meticulously numbered and documented, in store boxes. Ray's *Historia Insectorum* was published in 1710, five years after his death, and was a landmark volume in English entomological recording. Ray was the first person to rear the purple hairstreak butterfly. Ray described only one British species of butterfly new to science. This was the mazarine blue (*Cyaniris semiargus*) from an Essex-caught specimen given to him by his friend Samuel Dale. This species is no longer found in Britain.

Dr Alan Maclean, a Colchester physician with an all-round interest in natural history, studied butterflies and moths in the first half of the 19th century. A favourite site for his butterfly hunting was High Woods, Colchester (now High Woods Country Park) and adjoining tracts of woodland. In Maclean's time the purple emperor was still fairly common in these woods and the doctor found eggs and larvae on sallow bushes in High Woods and also at Dedham and Langham. He told his friends of his pleasure at seeing the male purple emperors soaring round the tops of the tallest oaks. Maclean was the first naturalist to make a thorough study of the hibernation of the larvae of the white admiral which, like the purple emperor, was still widespread in the woods of NE Essex in the 19th century.
Maclean, who designed and made a collapsible and folding butterfly net, died in 1869 and during his lifetime gained a certain amount of local notoriety for eccentricity. While out on his medical rounds in the Colchester area in a pony and trap he always carried one of his folding nets and there is a contemporary description of the "bug hunting" medico, top-hatted and swallowtail-coated, leaping from the trap to try and net a butterfly in Colchester High Street, near the old St Runwalds Church (long demolished). His quarry was said to be a Camberwell beauty but it was not recorded if he was successful on this occasion. He carried his net on his rounds to patients tucked into his capacious coat.

Miss Laetitia Jermyn, an Ipswich lepidopterist who also collected and recorded butterflies and moths in NE Essex, wrote a charming little book entitled *The Butterfly Collector's Vade Mecum* in 1827. When she was nearly 40, in 1832, she married James Ford, vicar of Navestock, Essex. They lived in Essex for nearly 18 years and Laetitia
104

continued her pursuit and recording of butterflies. She died in July,1848, and her clergyman husband survived her for only 18 months. Something of the spirit of this remarkable woman naturalist can be observed in the preface of her book where she defends butterfly collecting against the scorn "of those who attach the study of natural history as a trifling and worthless pursuit". The Synoptical table in her book provides a valuable reference source to North East Essex species and their distribution at that time. Purple emperor localities were given as Great and Little Stour Woods, Wrabness and in woods at Ramsey. She stated that the Duke of Burgundy fritillary (*Hamearis lucina*), long since vanished from Essex, was present in Bromley Thickets and at Hartley Wood, St Osyth. Laetitia also stated that the marbled white, these days confined to south Essex and Thames-side, occurred on Mersea Island and also in moist woodland rides at St Osyth. The delicate little wood white, another long-vanished Essex woodland species, was still to be seen at Wrabness, St Osyth (presumably Hartley Wood) and at Great Bromley.

William Henry Harwood was the most distinguished locally-born lepidopterist of the Victorian period. Born in February 1840, Harwood was a true pioneer who has not received the recognition his painstaking field work and careful recording deserve. He was the first person to perfect the technique of caterpillar rearing known as "sleeving" under which the larvae are in muslin or netting sleeves or tubes placed over growing tree and bush branches. For well over half a century from the 1850s until his death in 1917 Harwood was a prominent personality in local and national entomological circles, helped by his two sons Bernard and Philip who also gained some eminence as zealous hunters and recorders of butterflies and moths. Harwood's main contribution to entomological literature was the Insect Section of the *Victoria County History of Essex* (1903) which covered the lepidoptera in 41 pages. When Harwood, a pupil of Colchester Royal Grammar School, left school he was apprenticed to a firm of chemists but this work didn't suit a young man intent on becoming a professional naturalist and dealer. Harwood's doctor at Colchester advised him, for health reasons, to take up outdoor work and he needed no second bidding. He set up at Colchester as a professional entomologist and collector of natural history specimens. Many of the butterflies and moths collected by Harwood and sons found their way into the collections of wealthy patrons of natural history such as the Hon. Charles Rothschild who bought aberrations or unusual varieties. Some of these are in the national collections of butterflies and moths maintained by the British Museum of Natural History or the Hope Department, Oxford. Others were figured by F.W.Frohawk in his books on British butterflies

Gervase Frederick Mathew was another eminent Essex lepidopterist of the Victorian period. He was a retired Paymaster-in-Chief of the Royal Navy who settled in retirement in Dovercourt after service which took him all round the world. It was before he left the Navy that Mathew made a discovery at Dovercourt in 1895 which perpetuates his name. Collecting wainscot moths on marshland he was convinced that specimens he had found were not common wainscots but a new and hitherto undescribed species. Later it was confirmed that the moths were of a new and unrecorded species and so Mathew was given the permanent credit with the award of his name to Mathew's wainscot. Mathew died at Dovercourt on the eve of his 86th birthday on 10 February, 1928. Until his final illness he had remained remarkably alert and active, collecting in the local woods and marshes and contributing notes to the entomological journals. It was estimated that between 1855 and 1925 he contributed over 300 papers and notes to journals and books. A male purple emperor, probably the last authentic Essex specimen, was caught by Mathew at Stour Wood, Wrabness and is one of a number of Mathew specimens in the Colchester Natural history Museum collections.

A. Donald Blaxill was the most important lepidopterist in the Colchester area between the two World Wars and in the post second war period. He was the mentor of Joe Firmin and Ian Rose and was the inaugural chairman of Colchester Natural History Society in 1953, later serving as its President for a number of years. His interest in butterflies took him to many parts of the British Isles and he was an enthusiastic rearer of butterfly and moth larvae. His local successes included the rearing of the large tortoiseshell, now considered extinct as a resident British species but which was reasonably common in North East Essex until the mid-1950s when it went into a dramatic decline throughout its range in East Anglia and South East England.
Donald Blaxill's fine butterfly collection, including a number of notable aberrations, is in the Colchester Museum's reference collection.

GLOSSARY of technical terms

abdomen : Rear part of a butterfly's body, consisting of ten segments (not all of which are visible), and bearing the sex organs at the tip (see fig. 1).

androconium (plural: androconia): Sometimes called the 'scent scales', these are scales on the wings of male butterflies which are connected to tiny glands in the wing membrane, and they release pheromones into the air during 'courtship'. The androconia are often confined to definite patches or marks on the wings of the males - sometimes along some of the veins, sometime as dark streaks or broader dark areas across the fore-wings.

antenna (plural: antennae): Often called 'feelers', these are long, filamentous appendages which project from the butterfly's head. In butterflies they usually broaden out towards the tip to form a club-shape. The antennae of moths are of various shapes, but not usually clubbed, as in the butterflies. The antennae are important sense organs, being very sensitive to scents, and also to touch and vibration.

chrysalis (plural: chrysalids): This is the so-called resting stage in the life history of a butterfly. During this stage it does not move (except to wiggle its abdomen if disturbed) or feed. However, internally a great deal is going on: the transformation from the caterpillar to the adult butterfly.

cocoon : When caterpillars are about to shed their skin for the last time and enter the chrysalis stage, they often spin a few threads of silk to hold the future chrysalis in place. However, in some species (and more commonly among the moths), a much more elaborate silken cover is constructed to protect the chrysalis. This is the cocoon.

disc, discal spot : The wing-veins of butterflies share a common basic pattern (see fig.1). From the base of each wing out towards the middle is an area free of veins. This is called the cell. The outer margin of this is a junction for several veins and is called the disc. In several species this is high-lighted by scales of a distinctive colour, forming a spot in the centre of the wing. This is the discal spot.

entomology (entomologist): Entomology is the study of insects. An entomologist is someone who has a special interest in this subject.

Instar : This is the technical term given to the stages (usually four or five) in the development of a caterpillar. The first instar is the stage between hatching from the egg and the first moult (ecdysis) of its 'skin'. It will then go through several more instars, until it completes its growth. This is the 'final instar', prior to forming the chrysalis.

larva (plural: larvae): This is the stage in an insect's life-history between hatching from the egg and becoming a pupa. It is the main stage during which intensive feeding and growth takes place. Most larvae have a fairly simple segmented structure. The caterpillar is the larval stage in the butterfly's life-history, and in this book we use the two terms interchangeably.

Lepidoptera (lepidopterist): Lepidoptera is the major sub-division ('Order') of the insects which includes both butterflies and moths.

ocellus (plural: ocelli): Insects may have two types of eye. In the case of butterflies, their main visual sense is provided by the large compound eyes which cover most of the surface of the head. However, there are also minute simple eyes which are sensitive to light intensity, and are also situated on the head. These are the ocelli.

palpus (plural: palpi): The palpi are two small 'pads' on the butterfly's head, below the eyes, and enclosing the proboscis when it is furled up. They are sensory organs, and provide the butterfly with part of its sense of taste.

phenology : This is the (study of) the time-sequences of the behaviour and development of living things. In the case of butterflies it refers to the timing of each stage in the life-history, and the flight-period of the adults.

pheromones : These are specialised chemicals which communicate messages through the sense of smell. They are particularly important in the courtship behaviour and sexual attraction between butterflies.

proboscis : This is the very long 'tongue' of the butterfly, which is tubular in shape, and kept furled up under the head when not in use. Its main use is to suck up nectar from flowers, but in some species liquid from decaying flesh, or water from puddles etc. may be imbibed. The proboscis is also extended and plays a part in the courtship behaviour of some species.

pupa (plural: pupae): This is the so-called resting stage in the development of insects. The pupal stage of the butterfly is termed the chrysalis, and we use the two terms interchangeably in this book.

thorax : This is the middle part, or 'chest', of the butterfly body. It contains the powerful muscles which operate the wings, and to which the wing-bases are attached. The legs are also attached to the thorax.

BIBLIOGRAPHY

Asher, J. et al. 2001 *The Millennium Atlas of Butterflies in Britain and Ireland.* Oxford: Oxford University.

Bailey, G. 1994 The Brown Argus Burgeons in Essex. *Butterfly Conservation News.* 57:24-5.

Benton, E. 1980 Butterflies of the University of Essex Campus. *Nature in North East Essex 1980.* Colchester: CNHS: 37-41.

Benton, E. 1981 Butterflies and Conservation on the University Campus. *Nature in North East Essex 1981.* Colchester: CNHS: 66-70.

Benton, E. 1982 Butterfly Watching in North Essex 1982. *Nature in North East Essex 1982.* Colchester: CNHS: 76-81.

Benton, E. 1983 Butterflies. A.J.Wake (ed.) *The Roman River Valley: A Special Report.* Colchester: CNHS: 108-114.

Benton, E. 1984a The Survival of the Grayling Butterfly *(H. semele)* in the Colchester Area. *Nature in North East Essex 1984.* Colchester: CNHS: 5-6.

Benton, E. 1984b The White Letter Hairstreak Butterfly in the Colchester Area. *Nature in North East Essex 1984.* Colchester: CNHS: 59-61.

Blaxill, A. D. 1978 The Large Tortoiseshell Butterfly: Some Personal Observations. *Nature in North-East Essex: Silver Jubilee Issue 1953-1978.* Colchester: CNHS: 23-6.

Burton, J. F. & Sparks, T. H. 2002 Flying Earlier in the Year: the Phenological Response of Butterflies and Moths to Climate Change. *British Wildlife.* 13, 5: 305-11.

Chapman, J. & André, P. 1777 *A Map of the County of Essex.*

Clark, J. T. & Hobday, S. M. 1966 The Lepidoptera of North-East Essex. *Essex Naturalist 1962-1966.* 31: 105-18.

Corke, D. 1997 *The Butterflies of Essex.* Wimbish: Lopinga.

Davies, M. 1986 The White-letter Hairstreak project. *Butterfly Conservation News 36: 29-33.*

Davies, M. 1992 The White-letter Hairstreak Butterfly. *Butterfly Conservation booklet 12.* Colchester: BBCS.

Dewick, A. J. 1951 Lepidoptera in East Essex 1950. *Essex Naturalist.* 28: 293.

Dewick, A. J. 1956a Lepidoptera at Bradwell-on-Sea in 1951. *Essex Naturalist 1951-1955.* 29:43-4.

Dewick, A. J. 1956b Lepidoptera in East Essex 1953. *Essex Naturalist 1951-1955.* 29: 206.

Douglas, J. W. 1842 Captures of Lepidoptera in July during an Excursion of Four Days between Walton-on-the-Naze and Brightlingsea. *Essex. Entomologist 1:* 384-5.

Emmet, A. M. 1987 Essex Lepidopterists. *The Essex Field Club Bulletin.* 35: 14-21.

Emmet, A. M. & Heath, J. (eds) 1990 *The Butterflies of Great Britain and Ireland.* Great Horkesley: Harley.

Emmet, A. M. & Pyman, G. A. 1985 *The Larger Moths and Butterflies of Essex.* London: Essex Field Club.

Firmin, J. 1962 The Silver-washed Fritillary Butterfly in North East Essex. *Nature in North East Essex.* Colchester: CNHS: 21-2.

Firmin, J. 1964/5 The Status of the Speckled Wood Butterfly in Essex. *Nature in North East Essex.* Colchester: CNHS: 2-4.

Firmin, J. 1970 The Butterflies of North Essex: A Comparison of Status 1907-1970. *Nature in North East Essex.* Colchester: CNHS: 8-16.

Firmin, J. 1972 A History of the Purple Emperor Butterfly (Apatura iris) in North Essex. *Nature in North East Essex.* Colchester: CNHS: 7-10.

Firmin, J. 1974 The Butterflies of Friday Wood and Donyland Woods. *Nature in North East Essex.* Colchester: CNHS: 19-25.

Firmin, J. et al. 1975 *A Guide to the Butterflies and Larger Moths of Essex.* Fingringhoe: Essex Naturalists' Trust.

Firmin, J. 1976 The Camberwell Beauty and Other Immigrant Lepidoptera in 1976. *Nature in North East Essex.* Colchester: CNHS: 10-1.

Firmin, J. 1978a Natural History of the Hilly Fields, Colchester. *Nature in North-East Essex: Silver Jubilee Issue 1953-1978.* Colchester: CNHS: 49-55.

Firmin, J. 1978b Return of the White Admiral Butterfly *(Limenitis camilla)* in North-East Essex. *Nature in North East Essex: Silver Jubilee Issue 1953-1978.* Colchester: CNHS: 21-2.

Firmin, J. 1978c The Grayling Butterfly in North East Essex. *Nature in North East Essex 1978.* Colchester: CNHS: 46-7.

Firmin, J. 1979 Butterflies in North Essex. *Nature in North East Essex 1979.* Colchester: CNHS: 23-7.

Firmin, J. 1980 The Butterflies of Friday Wood, Berechurch. *Nature in North East Essex 1980.* Colchester: CNHS: 58-60.

Firmin, J. 1982a Spectacular Immigrations of the Painted Lady Butterfly. *Nature in North East Essex 1982.* Colchester: CNHS: 8-9.

Firmin, J. 1982b The Small Tortoiseshell Butterfly - Unusual Aberrations of a Large Second Brood. *Nature in North East Essex 1982.* Colchester: CNHS: 30-1.

Firmin, J. 1984 Immigration of the Clouded Yellow 1983. *Nature in North East Essex 1984.* Colchester: CNHS: 32.

Firmin, J. 1986a Speckled Wood Extends Range. *Nature in North East Essex 1986.* Colchester: CNHS: 17.

Firmin, J. 1986b Recovery of the Brown Argus Butterfly *(Aricia agestis Schiff)* in North Essex. *Nature in North East Essex 1986.* Colchester: CNHS: 44.

Firmin, J. 1988a   Recovery of the Wall Brown Butterfly. *Nature in North East Essex 1987.* Colchester: CNHS: 33.

Firmin, J. 1988b   Immigration of the Painted Lady. *Nature in North East Essex 1987.* Colchester: CNHS: 34.

Firmin, J. 1990a   Two Recovery Years for the Wall Brown Butterfly (*Lasiommata megera L.*). *Nature in North East Essex 1990.* Colchester: CNHS: 28.

Firmin, J. 1990b   Population 'Explosion' of the Holly Blue Butterfly (*Celastrina argiolus britanna* Verity). *Nature in North East Essex 1990.* Colchester: CNHS: 31.

Firmin, J. 1995a   Butterflies in North East Essex. *Nature in North East Essex 1993.* Colchester: CNHS: 23-5.

Firmin, J. 1995b   Clouded Yellow Butterflies (*Colias croceus*) in North East Essex in 1994. *Nature in North East Essex 1993.* Colchester: CNHS: 25.

Firmin, J. 1999a   Spectacular Increase in the Brown Argus Butterfly (*Aricia agestis* D.& S.) in NE Essex from 1993. *Nature in North East Essex 1993-1997.* Colchester: CNHS: 62-3.

Firmin, J. 1999b   Return of the White Admiral (*Ladoga camilla L.*) at Friday Wood. *Nature in North East Essex 1993-1997.* Colchester: CNHS: 63.

Firmin, J. 2001a   Woodland Butterfly Reintroduction Project. *Nature in North East Essex 2001.* Colchester: CHNS: 40.

Firmin, J. 2001b   Clouded Yellow Butterflies Plentiful in Year 2000. *Nature in North East Essex 2001.* Colchester: CNHS: 41.

Firmin, J. & Goodey, B. 2001   The Changing State of North East Essex Lepidoptera. *Nature in North East Essex 2001.* Colchester: CNHS: 36-9.

Fitch, A. E. 1891   *The Lepidoptera of Essex, pt. 1 - Butterflies.* Essex Naturalist. V: 74-108.

Fountaine, M. 1982   *Love Among the Butterflies.* London: Penguin.

Friedlein, J. T. 1951   North Fambridge Butterflies in 1950. *Essex Naturalist.* 28: 294.

Friedlein, J. T. 1956   Butterflies at North Fambridge in 1951. *Essex Naturalist 1951-1955.* 29: 44-5.

Friedlein, J. T. 1961   Butterflies and Moths at North Fambridge in 1956. *Essex Naturalist 1956-60.* 30: 71.

Frohawk, F. W. 1914   *Natural History of British Butterflies. Vol. 1.* London: Hutchinson.

Gibson, C.   Moth and Butterfly Records 1999 - TM226 304. *Nature in North East Essex 2001.* Colchester: CNHS: 43-65.

Goodey, B. 1985   Lepidoptera of Friday Wood, Berechurch. *Nature in North East Essex 1985.* Colchester: CNHS: 44-51.

Goodey, B. 1987   The Plight of the Grayling as an Essex Species. *Nature in North East Essex.* Colchester: CNHS: 58-60.

Goodey, B. 1995 The Larger Moths and Butterflies of Essex: A Selection of Recent Records. *The Essex Naturalist 12: 5-16.*

Goodey, B. 1996 Macrolepidoptera in Essex. *The Essex Naturalist (New Series)* 13: 17-9.

Goodey, B. 1997 Review of the Macrolepidoptera of Essex for the Year 1996. *The Essex Naturalist (New Series)* 14: 21-7.

Goodey, B. 1998 Review of the Lepidoptera of Essex for the Year 1997. *The Essex Naturalist (New Series)* 15: 23-32.

Goodey, B 1999a Lepidoptera Review of North East Essex from 1993 to 1997. *Nature in North East Essex 1993-1997.* Colchester: CNHS: 54-62.

Goodey, B. 1999b Review of the Lepidoptera of Essex for the Year 1998. *The Essex Naturalist (New Series).* 16: 45-52.

Goodey, B. 2000 Review of the Lepidoptera of Essex for 1999. *The Essex Naturalist (New Series).* 17: 86-96.

Goodey, B. 2001 Review of the Lepidoptera of Essex for the Year 2000. *The Essex Naturalist (New Series).* 18: 95-100.

Goodey, B. and Firmin, J. 1992 Lepidoptera in North East Essex. *Nature in North East Essex Special Issue.* Colchester: CNHS.

Gunton, T. 2000 *Wild Essex.* Wimbish: Lopinga.

Hall, M. L. 1981 *Butterfly Research in I.T.E.* Cambridge: Institute of Terrestrial Ecology.

Harwood, W. H. 1884 Letter quoted in Journal of Proceedings of the Essex Field Club. *Transactions of the Essex Field Club Vol. III: xxvii*

Harwood, W. H. 1903 Insects. *The Victoria History of the Counties of England: Essex. Vol. 3.* Westminster: Constable.

Hawes, F. W. 1890 *Hesperia lineola,* Ochsenheimer: An Addition to the List of British Butterflies. *The Entomologist.* 23: 3-4.

Hawes, F. W. 1892 On the Earlier Stages of Hesperia Lineola. *The Entomologist* 25: 177-80.

Huggins, H. C. 1956 A Survey of Essex Lepidoptera in the last 50 Years. *Essex Naturalist 1951-1955.* 29: 327-30.

Jermyn, L. 1827 *The Butterfly Collector's Vade Mecum.* Ipswich: J. Raw.

Mathew, G. F. 1892 *Hesperia lineola* at Harwich. *The Entomologist.* 25: 17.

Newman, E. 1870 *The Illustrated Natural History of British Butterflies and Moths.* London: W. H. Allen.

Newman, E. 1871 *British Butterflies.* London: William Tweedie.

Oates, M. 1984 An Introduction to the Ecology and Habits of the White-letter Hairstreak. *Butterfly Conservation News* 32: 36-41.

Ordnance Survey 1880 6" scale, North-east Essex sheets.

Ordnance Survey 1998 Explorer 184 & 195 (1:25,000). Southampton: O. S.

Pollard 1979   Population Ecology and Changes in Range of the White Admiral Butterfly *Ladoga camilla* L. in England. *Ecological Entomology* 4: 61-74.

Pollard, E. & Cooke, A. S. 1994 Impact of Muntjac Deer *Muntiacus reevesi* on Egg-laying Sites of the White Admiral Butterfly *Ladoga camilla* in a Cambridgeshire Wood. *Biological Conservation* 70: 189-91.

Pratt, C. B. 1956 The Speckled Wood Butterfly *(Pararge aegeria L.)* in Essex. *Essex Naturalist 1951-1955.* 29: 207-9.

Pye, M, Gardiner, T. & Field, R. 2002 Utilisation of Grassland refuges on Agricultural Land by Small Skipper *Thymelicus sylvestris* Poda and Essex Skipper *Thymelicus lineola* Ochs. (*Lep. Hesperiidae*). *Entomologists' Record, forthcoming.*

Pyman, G. A. 1983 The Fall and Rise of the Speckled Wood Butterfly in Essex. *The Essex Field Club Bulletin.* 28: 7-9.

Pyman, G. A. 1987 The Larger Moths and Butterflies of Essex: A Selection of Recent Records. *The Essex Field Club Bulletin.* 35: 25-38.

Ray, J. 1710   *Historia Insectorum.* London: A. & J. Churchill.

Raynor, G. H. 1884 The Macro-Lepidoptera of the District Around Maldon, Essex. *Transactions of the Essex Field Club Vol III:* 30-47.

Revels, R. 1994   The Rise and Fall of the Holly Blue Butterfly. *British Wildlife 5,* 4: 236-9.

Spiller, A. J. 1890 On the Occurrence of *Hesperia lineola* in Essex. *The Entomologist.* 23: 56-7.

Stace, C. 1997   *New Flora of the British Isles.* Cambridge: Cambridge University.

Steel, C. 1984   The White-letter Hairstreak Survey. *Butterfly Conservation News* 32: 31-5.

Tarpey, T and Heath, J. 1990 *Wild Flowers of North East Essex.* Colchester: CNHS.

Thomas, J. 1986 *RSNC Guide to Butterflies of the British Isles.* Twickenham: Hamlyn.

Thomas, J. & Lewington, R. 1991 *The Butterflies of Britain and Ireland.* London: Kindersley.

Urquhart, D. 2001 East Mersea Clouded Yellows - 2000. *Nature in North East Essex 2001.* Colchester: CNHS: 42.

Wake, A. J. (ed.) 1983 The Roman River Valley: A Special Report. *Nature in North East Essex 1983.* Colchester: CNHS.

Walley, P. 1980 *Butterfly Watching.* London: Severn House.

Watts, B. & McIlwrath, B. J. 2002 *Millennium Atlas of Norfolk Butterflies.* Norfolk: Butterfly Conservation, Norfolk Branch

Checklist

Species	Date	Where Seen	Date	Where Seen
Small skipper				
Essex skipper				
Large skipper				
Brimstone				
Large white				
Small white				
Green-veined white				
Bath white				
Orange-tip				
Clouded yellow				
Pale clouded yellow				
Berger's clouded yellow				
Green hairstreak				
Purple hairstreak				
White-letter hairstreak				
Small copper				
Long-tailed blue				
Brown argus				
Common blue				
Holly blue				
White admiral				
Camberwell beauty				
Small tortoiseshell				
Peacock				
Red admiral				
Comma				
Painted lady				
Silver-washed fritillary				
Queen of Spain fritillary				
Speckled wood				
Wall				
Marbled white				
Gatekeeper				
Meadow brown				
Ringlet				
Small heath				

THE AUTHORS

Ted Benton is Professor of Sociology at Essex University, specialising in environmental issues. He has been studying butterflies and other insects in the Colchester area for more than 30 years, publishing two book-length studies (Dragonflies of Essex (EFC 1988) and Bumblebees of Essex (Lopinga, 2000), and many articles. His photographs of European butterflies have been published in numerous books and magazines, and he is currently working on a photographic guide to European butterflies. He is a former chair of Colchester Natural History Society.

Joe Firmin, one of the founders of Colchester Natural History Society in 1953, has studied and recorded butterflies and their life histories in his native North East Essex for over half a century. Like Ted Benton he has also travelled extensively in Europe, especially France, to see and record butterflies and study their habitat requirements and conservation. Joe is chairman of Essex Moth Group, which he helped to form in 1996, and has been chairman of Essex Lepidoptera Panel since its formation in 1971.

Ian C. Rose, whose close-up colour photos illustrate this book with those of his friend and colleague Dr Ted Benton, is one of the best-known nature photographers in the eastern counties. He has travelled extensively on wildlife photographic expeditions including trips to Asia, North and South America, Africa and Galapagos as well as in Europe. Ian, as well as being an acknowledged expert on fungi, has also specialised in the study and photography of butterflies and moths and their life histories and is photographic editor for the Essex Moth Group, of which he was a founder-member in 1996. He is in great demand as a lecturer throughout East Anglia.